学做中国菜
Learn to Cook Chinese Dishes
肉菜类　　Meat Dishes

外　文　出　版　社
FOREIGN LANGUAGES PRESS

前　言

朱熙钧

倘若不是想成为专业厨师，只是为了自家享用和偶尔待客而学做中国菜，大可不必专门去拜师学艺。中国主妇的厨艺最初几乎都是从她们的老祖母或母亲那里耳濡目染学来的；待到为人妻母之后，她们之中的一些有心人，或借助菜谱潜心揣摩，或与友邻切磋交流，烹制出的菜馔有时竟然不逊于名店名厨的出品。当然，中国家庭中擅长烹饪的男士也比比皆是，而且饭店餐馆中的名厨以男性居多。

《学做中国菜》丛书的编撰者都是久在名店主厨的烹饪大师。为了使初学者易于入门，他们化繁为简，介绍了各类菜式的用料、刀法、制作步骤等；初学者只需按书中所列一一去做，无须多日便可熟能生巧，举一反三，厨艺大进。

《学做中国菜》丛书共9册，分水产类、菜蔬类、禽蛋类、肉菜类、米面类、汤菜类、冷菜类、豆品类、家宴类。本册为肉菜类分册，介绍40种肉类菜肴的用料和烹饪方法。

肉类菜肴一般是指用猪肉、羊肉、牛肉制作的菜肴。

猪肉因肌体各部位不同，肉质有肥、瘦、老、嫩之分因而原料使用更有广泛性，配料有互补性。可以大块烧煮，更可切成片、丝、粒、丁，与配料一起烹饪而成菜肴。羊肉肥肉多而瘦肉少，纤维长短不一，肉中多夹筋，基本上不能切丝，切成大块烧煮，或者切片爆炒，或涮后配以调料食用。牛肉瘦肉多，肉质较猪肉、羊肉老，因而适宜大块烧煮，也可切丝、切片或用作牛排。但切丝时必须沿纤维纹理的横断面切。

煸、炒、溜、炸猪肉丝片或牛肉丝等，基本上要挂蛋清、淀粉，使肉汁水分不致在油温升高时丧失而保持其鲜嫩。

肉类的烹饪一般是在烹制过程中加调料、配料而成，不同于煮熟后由进食者自己加配调料的方法。这是中国菜制作的特点。因而肉类烹调就要求有原汁、能入味。烹制大块肉类一般是加水后加热，使大量的脂肪、蛋白质、维生素及其他营养物质由于受热分解而溶解在水中成为鲜美的汤汁。烧煮时间以三小时为最佳，这样才能使原料入味。如樱桃肉以猪肉为原料，皮肉剖成小方块，加好调料蒸煮，直至酥烂而不脱型，并使原汁入味。又如红烧狮子头，是以肥四、精六之比的猪肉剁成肉茸，加以调料做成肉圆，入油锅用旺火煎黄后，再加调料、白汤烧沸，转小火烧半小时左右方成，故而能入味，鲜香而又肥而不腻。即使是酸甜可口的咕噜肉，也是先将猪肉片，用调料烹制入味后，再用酸甜调料和肉汤煞浓后与其一起翻炒，使调料的味道渗入其中。

肉类的烹制方法很多，炸、溜、烹、爆、炒、煸、烤几乎全可用上。制作时，需根据食用者的喜好和口味选择菜式及相应的烹制方法。

Foreword

Zhu Xijun

You don't have to take classes from a professional teacher to learn the art of Chinese cooking if all you want to do is to entertain your friends or cook for your family. Almost without exception, Chinese women learn this skill by watching and working together with their mothers or grandmothers. After they become wives or mothers themselves, the most diligent will try to improve their techniques by consulting cook books and exchanging experiences with their neighbors. In this way they eventually become as skilled as the best chefs in established restaurants. It should be noted, of course, that most of the well-known chefs in famous restaurants are men, because many men in Chinese homes are just as good at the art of cooking as their wives.

This book in the *Learn to Cook Chinese Dishes* series has been compiled by master chefs. They use simple explanations to introduce the ingredients, the ways of cutting, and the cooking procedures for each recipe. Readers, who follow the directions, will become skilled before long in the art of Chinese cooking. The entire set consists of nine volumes, covering freshwater and seafood dishes, meat dishes, vegetable dishes, courses made from soy beans, soups, cold dishes, pastries, dishes of eggs and poultry, and recipes for family feasts. This volume presents forty meat dish recipes.

Meat dishes in Chinese cooking generally refer to those dishes using pork, lamb or mutton and beef as the main ingredient. Pork, because of the different qualities of the meat, being fat, lean, tough and tender and coming from different parts of the pig, provides a wide range of choices. Other ingredients that are used in cooking with pork compliment the particular choice of meat. Pork can be cut in large chunks, or it can be cut into slices, shreds, or cubes to be used in dishes with other ingredients. Mutton is not generally cut into shreds because of its wide spread of sinew, different length of fiber and greater amount of fat. Ideally, it is stewed in large chunks or quickly stir-fried in slices. It provides a good choice for a hot pot, along with other ingredients. Beef has more lean meat than fat and is usually tougher than pork or mutton. It is thus most suitable for stewing in large pieces or for cutting into shreds and slices. Of course it is good material for making steaks. When cutting beef, make sure you cut against the grain of the meat.

To stir-fry, quick-fry and braise beef or pork shreds, egg white or cornstarch usually has to be used to mix with the cut meat so that the juices in the meat will not be entirely lost during the process of cooking over a high fire. This also preserves the tenderness of the meat.

Spices and seasonings are usually added in the process of cooking, rather than having the meat cooked first and then adding the seasonings at the time of serving. This is one of the major characteristics of Chinese cooking. It is therefore very important to preserve the original juice of the meat and let the flavor of the seasonings be totally absorbed. To cook large pieces of meat, add water first and heat it so that much of the fat, protein, vitamins and other nutrients will dissolve into the water to make a delicious soup or gravy. Three hours of cooking is ideal in order to allow all the flavors to be absorbed into the dish. For example, one dish uses pork, both the meat and skin parts, cut into small squares and boiled along with the seasonings. The meat tastes soft, juicy and simply delicious. Another, "Stewed Large Pork Balls with Brown Sauce" requires a mixture of 60 percent lean meat and 40 percent fatty meat ground and shaped into balls, after all the necessary ingredients are added. Then the pork balls are deep-fried over a high fire until they are brownish in color. More seasonings and ingredients are boiled along with the meatballs. Once the liquid boils, a low fire is used to let the dish simmer for 30 minutes. This way, the dish is rich but not greasy and the flavors are fully absorbed into the meatballs. Even to cook "Sweet and Sour Pork", the meat must be sliced and first cooked along with seasonings. More sweet and sour seasonings and soup are used to make thick gravy. This gravy is then used to stir-fry with the previously cooked pork slices in order to allow the maximum absorption of the flavors.

There are many ways of cooking meat dishes, including deep-frying, slippery-frying, quick-frying, stir-frying after the meat is submerged in previously prepared sauce, deep-frying before stir-frying, braising, and roasting. Each depends on the wishes of the diner when choosing the ingredients and ways of cooking.

目　录
Contents

名词解释
Terms Used in Chinese Cooking ·················· (1)

五彩牛肉丝
Five-color Shredded Beef ·················· (8)

酥炸牛肉丸
Flaky Deep-fried Beef Balls ·················· (10)

核桃牛肉
Beef with Walnuts ·················· (12)

豉汁牛肉
Beef with Black Bean Sauce ·················· (14)

蚝油牛肉
Beef with Oyster Sauce ·················· (16)

家乡牛肉
Home-style Beef ·················· (18)

红焖牛肉
Braised Beef with Soy Sauce ·················· (20)

仔姜牛肉丝
Shredded Beef with Fresh Ginger ·················· (22)

芝麻牛排
Beef Fillet with Sesame ·················· (24)

香酥牛肉卷
Crispy Beef Roll ·················· (26)

菠萝牛肉
Sliced Beef with Pineapple ·················· (28)

脆皮牛肉
Deep-fried Crispy Beef ·················· (30)

葱爆羊肉片
Mutton Slices with Scallions ·················· (32)

红烧狮子头
Stewed Large Pork Balls with Brown Sauce ·········· (34)

滑溜里脊
Slippery-fried Pork Tenderloin ·················· (36)

咸蛋蒸肉饼
Steamed Pork with Salted Eggs ·················· (38)

冬笋肉丝
Shredded Pork with Winter Bamboo Shoots ··········· (40)

梅干菜扣肉
Twice-cooked Pork with Preserved Vegetable ········ (42)

京都金排骨
Capital-style Pork Ribs ·················· (44)

炒三丁
Triple Cubes ·················· (46)

红烧排骨
Pork Ribs in Brown Sauce ·················· (48)

回锅肉片
Twice-cooked Pork with Spicy Sauce ·················· (50)

青椒肉丝
Shredded Pork with Green Peppers ·················· (52)

麻辣肉片
Spicy Sliced Pork ·················· (54)

米粉蒸肉
Steamed Pork Slices with Glutinous Rice ·············· (56)

辣子肉丁
Stir-fried Diced Pork with Green Pepper ·············· (58)

虎皮肉
Tiger-skin Pork ······························· (60)

五彩肉丝
Five-color Shredded Pork ···················· (62)

红烧肉
Braised Pork with Brown Sauce ·············· (64)

咕噜肉
Sweet and Sour Pork ······················· (66)

椒盐排骨
Fried Pork Ribs with Pepper Salt ············ (68)

脆炸肉饼
Deep-fried Crispy Pork Cakes ·············· (70)

鱼香肉丝
Stir-fried Shredded Pork with Chili ·········· (72)

糖醋肉排
Fried Pork Fillet with Sweet and Sour Sauce ········· (74)

木樨肉
Stir-fried Pork Slices with Eggs and Fungi ·········· (76)

宫保肉丁
Stir-fried Diced Pork with Chili ······················ (78)

腐乳肉
Stewed Pork with Preserved Bean Curd ············· (80)

五香肉排
Spicy Pork Ribs ··································· (82)

鸡蛋肉粒烩粟米
Diced Pork with Corn and Egg ······················ (84)

肉丝跑蛋
Shredded Pork with Egg ·························· (86)

计量换算表
A comparison of the weight systems and a conversion
table for measuring Chinese cooking ingredients ······ (88)

名词解释 Terms Used in Chinese Cooking

上浆：猪肉丝、猪肉片、牛肉丝、牛肉片、羊肉丝、羊肉片、鸡肉片在烹制前都要上浆。上浆大多用于滑溜、滑炒、清炒、酱爆等烹调方法。上浆好坏，直接影响烹调出菜肴的质量。上浆就是把切好的肉，用水冲洗净，放入盐、料酒、淀粉(有时也放鸡蛋)，拌匀后，向一个方向搅拌，感到有劲为止。

Coating (*shangjiang*): Shreds and slices of pork, beef, mutton and chicken have to be coated before they are cooked in such ways as slippery-frying, quick-frying and stir-frying. And how the meat is coated has a direct bearing on the quality of the cooked dish. The coating process involves first washing the cut meat, then adding in salt, cooking wine, and cornstarch(sometimes eggs are also used) and stiring well in the same direction until you feel it is a bit sticky.

刀工 Cutting techniques:

直刀法：就是指刀同砧板垂直的刀法，分切、剁、砍，切是一般用于无骨的主料，剁是将无骨的主料制成茸的一种刀法，砍通常用于加工带骨的或硬的主料。

Straight-cutting: Holding the knife perpendicularly over the chopping board to cut, chop and heavy-cut the main ingredient. Cutting is applied to boneless meat ingredients, chopping is done to turn boneless ingredients into pulp or paste and heavy-cutting is used when preparing meat with bones or other hard ingredients.

平刀法：是刀面与砧板平行的一种刀法，分推刀、拉刀。推刀就是把刀从刀尖一直推到刀根，拉刀就是把刀从刀根拉到刀尖。平切就是把刀一切到底。

Horizontal-cutting: Holding the knife flat against the chopping board to push it or pull it through the ingredients.Pushing means to push the knife through the ingredients from the knife's tip through to its end while pulling involves going through the ingredients from the end to the tip of the knife.

斜刀法：刀面同砧板面成小于 90 度夹角的刀法。

Slashing: To cut by holding the knife in an angle smaller than 90 degrees from the surface of the chopping board.

花刀：是在主料表面用横、竖两种刀法的不同变化，切(不断)出花纹，经加热后，主料卷曲成各种形状的刀法，有菊花形花刀，麦穗刀，鳞毛形花刀等。

Mixed cutting: To cut straight and then cross with sideways cuts to produce varied patterns. When heated, the ingredients cut in this way will roll up into different forms such as chrysanthemums, wheat ears and scales, according to the ways they are cut.

片：用切或片的方法将原料加工成薄片。质地硬的原料用切，质地软的用片的方法加工成薄片。

Slicing (*pian*): By either cutting or slicing to turn the ingredients into thin slices. Hard ingredients require cutting while soft ingredients require slicing.

丝：丝有粗细之分，一般在0.2-0.4厘米左右。一般先将主料切成0.2-0.4厘米的薄片，再将这些薄片排成瓦楞状，排叠要整齐，左手按稳主料，不可滑动，用刀把主料切成丝。

Shredding (*si*): The thickness of shreds usually varies between 0.2 (0±08 in) and 0.4 cm (0±16 in). First, either chunks of meat or vegetables are cut into thin slices of 0.2 to 0.4 cm in thickness. The slices are then arranged neatly like roof tiles. Pressed steadily underneath the left hand of the chef, the slices are finally cut into shreds.

条：条的成形方法，是先把主料切成厚片，再将片切成条，条的粗细取决于片的厚薄。

Strapping (*tiao*): Main raw materials are cut into thick slices that are cut again into straps the size of which is decided by the thickness of the slices.

粒：粒比丁小些一般在0.3厘米见方，切的方法同丁相同。

Grain-sized dicing (*li*): Cut in the same way as diced pieces, they are simply much smaller in size. The most common size is 0.3 cm (0.12 in) each side.

丁：先将主料切成厚片，再将厚片切成条，然后再切成丁。丁有大小之分，大丁在2厘米见方，小丁在1厘米见方。

Dicing (*ding*): Main raw materials are cut into thick slices that are cut into straps. In turn, the straps are reduced to diced pieces that may be as large as 2 cm (0.8in) on each side or as small as 1 cm (0.39 in) on each side.

末：末比粒还小，将丁或粒剁碎就可以了。

Mincing (*mo*): Ground ingredients are even smaller than grain-sized dices. Usually the diced pieces are chopped into mince.

茸：用排剁的方法把主料剁得比末还细。

Chopping to make a pulp (*rong*): To chop the materials, knife cut after knife cut into pieces even finer than minced materials.

块：块是采用切、砍、剁等刀法加工而成的。块分菱形块、方块、长方块、滚刀块等。

Cutting into chunks (*kuai*): Chunks are the result of perpendicular and sideways cutting as well as chopping. The chunks come in many shapes such as diamonds, squares and rectangles.

炸：是旺火加热，以食油为传热介质烹调方法，特点是火旺用油量多。

Deep-frying (*zha*): Heat the cooking oil over a hot fire and deep-fry the materials. This process is characterized by a hot fire and a large amount of oil.

炒：炒是将加工成丁、丝、条、球等小型主料投入油锅中，在旺火上急速翻炒成熟的一种烹调方法。炒分滑炒、熟炒、干炒等几种。滑炒是经过粗加工的小型主料先经上浆，再用少量油在旺火上急速翻炒，最后以湿淀粉勾芡的方法，叫滑炒。熟炒是把经过初步加工后的半成品，改切成片或块，不上浆，用旺火烧锅热油，放入半成品翻炒，再加佐料而成。煸炒和干炒是把主料煸一下，在热油锅急火炒至退水后，加佐料，起锅。

Stir-frying (*chao*): Put processed materials in the shape of diced pieces, shreds, straps, or balls into the heated oil and quickly stir them over a hot fire. There are several different ways of stir-frying. *Hua chao* (stir-frying with batter), for example, requires that the ingredients are put in a batter and then quickly stirred in a small quantity of oil over a hot fire.The final process is to apply the mixture of cornstarch and water. *Shu chao* (stir-frying precooked food) does not require that the materials be put into some kind of batter. Simply put the precooked materials into the wok and use a hot fire before adding spicing agents. *Bian chao* and *gan chao* (raw stir-frying) calls for the simmering of main ingredients, then quick-stir-frying over a hot fire until the juice is fully absorbed. Now add spicing agents and the dish is ready to serve.

溜：溜是先将主料用炸的方法加热成熟，然后把调制好的卤汁浇淋于主料上，或将主料投入卤汁中搅拌的一种烹调方法。
Slippery-frying(*liu*): First deep-fry the main ingredient and then top it with sauce or mix the main ingredient in the sauce.

爆：爆是将脆性主料投入适量的油锅中，用旺火高油温快速加热的一种烹调方法。
Quick-fry over high heat (*bao*): Put crispy materials into the wok with medium amount of oil and quickly stir the materials over high heat.

隔水炖：隔水加热使主料成熟的方法，叫做隔水炖。
Steaming in a container (*ge shui dun*): Put the main ingredient into a bowl or similar container and cook it in a steamer.

烧：烧是经过炸、煎、煸炒或水煮的主料，再用葱姜炝锅后，倒入翻炒，然后加适量汤水和调味品，用旺火烧开，中小火烧透入味 ，改用旺火使卤汁稠浓的一种烹调方法。
Stewing over medium,then high heat (*shao*): After putting scallions and ginger into the wok, put in the main materials that have been deep-fried, or stir-fried or boiled and stirred. Then add water and seasoning materials to cook over a hot fire until the ingredients boil. Turn the fire to medium or low to allow full absorption of the sauce into the ingredients before turning the fire hot again to thicken the sauce.

扒：扒是将经过初步熟处理的主料整齐地排放在锅内，加汤汁和调味品，用旺火烧开，小火烧透入味，出锅前，原汁勾芡的一种烹调方法。
Stewing and adding thickening (*pa*): Neatly arrange the main ingredient that has already been cooked,add water and flavoring materials and cook over a hot fire until it boils. Turn the fire to low to allow full absorption of the flavor. Thicken the sauce with the mixture of water and cornstarch before bringing the dish out of the wok to serve.

煮：煮是将主料放入多量的汤汁或水中，先用旺火煮沸，再用中小火烧熟的一种烹调方法。
Boiling (*zhu*): Put main materials of the dish into the wok with an adequate amount of water and cook it over a hot fire to the boiling point. Then continue to cook after turning the fire to low or medium.

烩：将加工成片、丝、条、丁等料的多种主料放在一起，炝锅翻炒后，用旺火制成半汤半菜的菜肴，这种烹调方法就是烩。
Precooking and then stewing (*hui*): First heat the oil in the wok, put in scallions and ginger and then put several kinds of main ingredients that have been cut into slices, shreds, chunks or dices to cook over a hot fire so as to create a dish of half soup and half vegetables and meat.

煎：煎是以少量油布遍锅底、用小火将主料煎熟使两面呈黄色的烹调方法。

Sauteing (*jian*): Put a small amount of oil into the wok and use a low fire to cook the main ingredient until it is golden brown on both sides.

蒸: 蒸是以蒸汽的热力使经过调味的主料成熟或酥烂入味的烹调方法。

Steaming (*zheng*): Cook the materials that have already been prepared with flavoring agents by using hot steam.

拔丝: 拔丝又叫拉丝，是将经过油炸的小型主料，挂上能拔出丝来的糖浆的一种烹调方法。

Crisp frying with syrup (*ba si*): Put small-size ingredients that have already been deep-fried into sugar syrup heated in the wok. When diners pick up the materials, long sugar threads are created.

焯水: 就是把经过初加工的主料，放在水锅中加热至沸(主要为去腥味或异味)，原料出水后供烹调菜肴之用。焯水分冷水锅和热水锅。冷水锅就是主料与冷水同时下锅，水沸取出，适用于腥气重血量多的主料如牛肉、羊肉等。热水锅就是先将锅中水加热至沸，再将主料下锅，翻滚后再取出主料。适用于腥气小，血污少的主料如鸡、鸭、猪肉和蔬菜。

Quick boiling (*chao*): Put main ingredients into the pot and heat the water to boiling point(in order to remove fishy or other undesirable smells). Then cook the boiled ingredients. The quick-boiling process includes cold water boiling and hot water boiling. The former requires putting the ingredients into the pot toge ther with the cold water and then taking them out when the water boils. This process is often applied to such materials as beef and mutton,which contain a fishy smell and a lot of blood. The latter calls for heating the water in the pot to boiling point before putting the ingredients in.This is applicable to materials like chicken, duck, pork and vegetables that have a much weaker fishy smell and less blood.

油温表

油温类型	俗　称	油温特点
温油锅	四成 70℃-100℃	无青烟，无响声，油面平静。
热油锅	五、六成热 110℃-170℃	微有青烟，油四周向内翻动。
旺油锅	七、八成热 180℃-220℃	有青烟，油面仍较平静，用勺搅动有响声。

Temperatures of cooking oil:

Category	Temperature	Features
Luke-warm	70ºC-100ºC 158ºF-212ºF	Smokeless, soundless, calm oil surface
Hot oil	110ºC-170ºC 230ºF-338ºF	Slight smoke, oil stirs from the side to the center of the wok
Very hot oil	180ºC-220ºC 356ºF-428ºF	Smokes, the surface remains calm and when stirred, sizzling sound is heard.

花椒: 花椒是花椒树的果实，以籽小，壳厚紫色为好。味香麻，烹调肉类的调料。

Prickly ash (*hua jiao*): Seeds from prickly ash trees, which are small and light purple in color. They have a slight effect of numbness on the tongue. Used to cook dishes with meat.

椒盐: 味香麻，是炸菜蘸食的调味品。把花椒和盐按1:3的比例在锅中，微火炒成焦黄，磨成细末，即成。

Pepper salt (*jiao yan*): This mixture is made by stirring one portion of peppercorns and three portions of salt in the wok until they turn crispy yellowish in color and release their fragrance. Then finely grind the mixture into powder. It serves as a seasoning for deep-fried dishes.

味精： 根据个人口味，也可不放味精，而使用适量的鸡精。
Monosodium glutamate and chicken bouillon: Though MSG is essential in traditional Chinese cooking, for many who do not find it agreeable, chicken bouillon can be used instead.

茴香： 小茴香是茴香菜的籽，呈灰色，似稻粒，有浓郁的香味。
Fennel seeds (*hui xiang*): Seeds of fennel plants, grey in color and similar to unhusked rice grains in shape, have a hot flavor.

大茴香： 又名八角、大料，形如星状，味甜浓，烹调肉类的调料。
Star anise (*da hui xiang*): In the shape of stars, they have a strong and sweet flavor. Mostly used in cooking meat dishes.

糟： 制作料酒剩下的酒糟经过加工就成为烹调用的糟，糟具有同料酒同样的调味作用。
Steaming with distillers'grains sauce (*zao*): Distillers'grains, which are left over from liquor making, are processed into a spicy agent for cooking that has the same function as the cooking wine.

五香料： 大料、茴香、桂皮、甘草、丁香(丁香花蕾)五种香料

混合为五香料，研成粉为五香粉。
Five Spices (*wu xiang liao*): A mixture of powdered star anise, fennel seed, cinnamon bark, licorice root and clove buds. Also referred to as the "five-powdered spices".

桂皮： 是桂树的皮，外皮粗糙呈现褐色。
Cinnamon (*gui pi*): The bark of cinnamon trees, brown in color.

料酒： 常用料酒是用糯米等粮食酿制成的，料酒，在烹调菜肴过程中起去腥、增香的作用，特别是烹制水产或肉类时少不了它。如没有料酒，可用适量的啤酒或白兰地代替，但没有料酒好。
Cooking wine (*liao jiu*): Cooking wine, brewed from grain, is applied to remove the fishy smell and increase the aroma of the dish. It is particularly essential when cooking dishes with aquatic ingredients and meat. While cooking wine is most desirable, in its absence, beer and brandy can be used.

勾芡： 勾芡就是在菜肴接近成熟时，将调好的湿淀粉加入锅内，搅拌均匀，使卤汁稠浓。增加卤汁对主料的附着力的一种方法。
Thickening with mixture of cornstarch and water (*gou qian*): When the dish is nearly cooked, put a previously prepared mixture

of cornstarch and water into the dish and stir well so as to thicken the sauce or broth. This process promotes the flavored sauce to stay with the main materials of the dish.

勾芡作用: 1、增加菜肴汤汁的粘性和浓度。2、增加菜肴的光泽。

Major functions of this process: (1) Increase the stickiness and thickness of the sauce of the dish. (2) Making the dish look more shiny.

勾芡关键: 1、勾芡必须在菜肴即将成熟时候进行。2、勾芡时锅中汤汁不可太多或太少。3、必须在菜肴的口味、颜色已经调准后进行。4、勾芡时锅中油不宜太多。

Key for using this process: (1) This process must be conducted when the cooking of the dish is nearly complete. (2) The sauce in the wok must not be too much or too little when this thickening technique is applied. (3) This process can only be done after all efforts for flavoring and coloring of the dish are completed. (4) When doing the thickening process, the wok should not have too much oil in it.

如何使用筷子

吃中式饭菜一般使用筷子。筷子是用木或竹、骨及其它材料制成长 25-30 厘米、上方(各边为 8 毫米)下圆(直径为 3-5 毫米)的二根小棍。

使用时须依靠拇指及食指、中指和无名指的连贯配合。方法是: 首先把两根筷子拿在右手,用食指、中指及无名指在距筷子近上端处各夹一根筷子,再把拇指和食指合在一起,如图1。用筷子取食时,把食指和中指夹的一根向上抬,另一根不动,使两根筷子张开。如图2。夹取食物时,把食指和中指夹的筷子往下压, 夹住食物,抬起筷子进食, 如图3。

How to Use Chopsticks

Chopsticks for eating Chinese food are usually made from wood, bamboo, animal bones or other materials. About 25 to 30

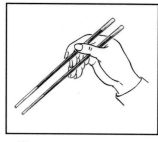

(1)

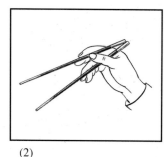

(2)

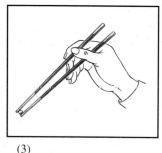

(3)

centimeters long, their top is square, about 0.8 square centimeter, and the low end round with a diameter of 3 to 5 millimeters.

The correct way of using the chopsticks requires concerted efforts of the thumb, index finger, middle finger and third finger. Hold the pair of chopsticks in the right hand, using the index finger, middle and third fingers to keep the chopsticks steady near their top and then push them open by moving the thumb and index finger. (See Drawing 1)

To pick things up with chopsticks, lift upward one of the two chopsticks with the index and middle fingers while keeping the other one where it is so as to separate the two. (See Drawing 2)

Once the chopsticks have picked up the food, press one of the chopsticks with the thumb and index finger and raise the pair. (See Drawing 3)

笼屉　蒸锅
Steaming tray(*long ti*)Usually made of bamboo or wood, these often come in several tiers

炒锅
Skillet

火锅
Hot-pot

砂锅
Earthen pot

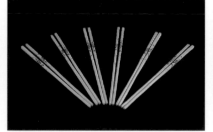

汤勺　炒铲　漏勺
Soup spoon Shovel Perforated spoon

筷子
Chopsticks

菜（面）板
Chopping board

五彩牛肉丝

主料：牛里脊 100 克

辅料：冬笋 75 克、洋葱 50 克、香菇 75 克、青辣椒和红辣椒各 25 克

调料：蒜茸 0.5 克、油 100 克(实耗 50 克)、清汤 25 克、湿淀粉 7.5 克、麻油 0.5 克、盐 5 克、味精 1 克、鸡蛋清 1 只、干淀粉 2 克

制作：①牛里脊切成长 6 厘米、宽和厚约 0.3 厘米的丝。冬笋、洋葱、香菇、辣椒切成与牛肉丝一样粗细的丝，待用。

②牛肉丝放入碗中，加盐 0.5 克，搅拌上劲，放鸡蛋清、干淀粉拌匀。

③将锅烧热放入油，待油烧至四成热时，将牛肉丝放入锅内滑炒至熟，倒在漏勺里沥油。

④锅中留余油 20 克放蒜茸及辅料炒透，倒入牛肉丝，加清汤烧沸，用湿淀粉勾芡，淋麻油炒匀，出锅装盘即可。

特点：色彩绚丽

口味：鲜香嫩滑

Five-color Shredded Beef

Ingredients:

100 grams (0.22 lb) beef tenderloin
75 grams (0.16 lb) bamboo roots
50 grams (0.11 lb) onions
75 grams (0.16 lb) mushrooms
25 grams (5/6 oz) green peppers
25 grams (5/6 oz) red peppers
0.5 gram (1/2 tsp) mashed garlic
100 grams (3 1/2 tbsp) oil (only half to be consumed)
25 grams (1 1/2 tbsp) water
7 1/2 grams (1 1/2 tsp) mixture of cornstarch and water
1/2 gram (1/10 tsp) sesame oil
5 grams (5/6 tsp) salt
1 gram (1/4 tsp) MSG
1 egg white
2 grams (2/5 tsp) dry cornstarch

Directions:

1. Cut the beef loin into strips 6 cm (2.4 inches) long, 0.3 cm (0.12 inch) thick and wide. Cut the bamboo shoots, onions, mushrooms, green and red peppers into shreds of similar size.

2. Put the beef strips in a bowl, add 1/2 g (1/12 tsp) of salt and stir until you feel it is sticky. Add the egg white and dry cornstarch and mix well.

3. Heat the oil in a wok to 70-100℃ (160-210˚F). Put in the beef strips and stir-fry until they are done. Take out and drain off the oil.

4. Keep 20 g (1 1/2 tbsp) of oil in the wok. Add the mashed garlic and all the other ingredients except the beef and stir well. Add the beef strips and water. Thicken this with the mixture of cornstarch and water and sprinkle on the sesame oil. Put on a plate and serve.

Features: Beautifully colored.
Taste: Tender, slippery and delicious.

五彩牛肉丝
Five-color Shredded Beef

酥炸牛肉丸

主料:牛肉 400 克

辅料:面粉 150 克、发酵粉 1 克

调料:味精 1 克、盐 5 克、干淀粉 20 克、胡椒粉 0.2 克、麻油 0.5 克、油 500 克(实耗 50 克)、水 100 克

制作:①将牛肉剁成末放入碗中,加盐、味精、胡椒粉搅拌上劲,加干淀粉拌匀并挤成鸽蛋大小的牛肉丸,上笼蒸熟待用。

②面粉和发酵粉用水调和成浆。

③将熟肉丸逐个浸入浆中,使肉丸外表粘匀汁浆。

④将锅烧热加入油,烧至八成热时,把粘上浆的肉丸逐个炸至色泽金黄,捞出装盘,淋上麻油即可。

特点:色泽金黄,外脆里嫩

口味:干香咸鲜

Flaky Deep-fried Beef Balls

Ingredients:
400 grams (0.88 lb) beef
150 grams (0.33 lb) wheat flour
1 gram (1/4 tsp) baking powder
1 gram (1/4 tsp) MSG
5 grams (5/6 tsp) salt
20 grams (2 tbsp) dry cornstarch
0.2 gram (1/20 tsp) pepper powder
0.5 gram (1/10 tsp) sesame oil
500 grams (1 cup) oil (only 1/10 of it to be consumed)
100 grams (6 tbsp) water

Directions:
1. Grind the beef into minced meat and put in a bowl. Add the salt, MSG, and pepper powder and stir well. Add the dry cornstarch and mix well. Shape the mixture into balls about the size of pigeon eggs. Steam for 15 minutes.

2. Use the flour and baking powder to make a paste.

3. One by one put the meatballs in the flour paste and totally cover them with the paste.

4. Heat the oil in a wok to 200-220℃ (390-430°F). Deep-fry the balls wrapped in flour paste until they are golden yellow in color. Place them on a plate and sprinkle the sesame oil over them. The dish is ready to serve.

Features: Golden yellow in color, crispy outside and tender inside.
Taste: Crispy, salty and delicious.

酥炸鲜牛肉丸
Flaky Deep-fried Beef Balls

核桃牛肉

主料：牛肉 300 克

辅料：核桃仁 100 克

调料：葱段 7.5 克、姜末 1.5 克、油 150 克、清汤 25 克、湿淀粉 10 克、胡椒粉 0.5 克、盐 3 克、味精 1.5 克、鸡蛋清 1 只、干淀粉 10 克

制作：①牛肉切成 1 厘米见方的丁，放盐 1 克和鸡蛋清搅拌上劲，加干淀粉拌匀。

②把核桃仁炸熟待用。

③将锅烧热放入油 100 克，烧至五成热时，倒入牛肉丁炒熟，捞出滤去油，余油继续加热，放入葱段、姜末煸出香味，放清汤烧沸，加盐、味精、胡椒粉，倒入肉丁、核桃仁，炒匀，用湿淀粉勾芡，出锅装盘。

特点：核桃脆香，牛肉滑嫩

口味：咸、鲜、香

Beef with Walnuts

Ingredients：

300 grams (0.66 lb) beef
100 grams (0.22 lb) shelled walnuts
1/2 grams (1/4 oz) scallions sectioned
15 grams (1/20 oz) ginger chopped
150 grams (11 tbsp) cooking oil
25 grams (1 1/2 tbsp) water
10 grams (2 tsp) mixture of cornstarch and water
1/2 gram (1/8 tsp) pepper powder
3 grams (1/2 tsp) salt
1 1/2 grams (1/3 tsp) MSG
1 egg white
10 grams (1 tbsp) dry cornstarch

Directions：

1. Cut the beef into cubes 1 cm (0.4 inch) wide. Add 1 g (1/6 tsp) salt and the egg white, and stir well until the mixture grows sticky. Add 10 g (1 tbsp) of dry cornstarch and mix well.

2. Deep-fry the walnuts.

3. Heat 100 g (7 tbsp) of oil in a wok to 110-135℃ (230-275˚F). Put in the beef cubes and stir-fry until they are done. Take out and drain off the oil. Heat the leftover oil in the wok to stir-fry the scallions and ginger until a distinctive aroma is achieved. Add the water and bring to boil. Add the salt, MSG, and pepper powder to the wok and then the beef cubes and walnuts. Stir-fry for about 1 to 2 minutes. Thicken the juice with the mixture of cornstarch and water. Now serve on a plate.

Features：The walnuts are crispy and tasty, and the beef is slippery and tender.
Taste：Salty and delicious.

核桃牛肉
Beef with Walnuts

豉汁牛肉

主料：牛肉 300 克

辅料：豆豉 5 克

调料：蒜茸 5 克、姜末 5 克、葱段 15 克、油 100 克、料酒 20 克、清汤 25 克、湿淀粉 10 克、干淀粉 10 克、鸡蛋清 1 只、胡椒粉 5 克、盐 3 克、味精 2 克

制作：①牛肉切成长 5 厘米、宽 3 厘米的薄片，放盐 1 克和鸡蛋清搅拌上劲，加干淀粉拌匀。

②将锅烧热，放入油 100 克，烧至四成热时，倒入牛肉片滑炒至熟，倒入漏勺里沥油。

③将油倒回锅内烧热，放入豆豉、蒜茸、姜末、葱段煸炒出香味，放料酒、清汤、盐、味精、胡椒粉烧沸，倒入牛肉片，用湿淀粉勾芡，淋上麻油，出锅装盘。

特点：色如象牙

口味：味香肉嫩

Beef with Black Bean Sauce

Ingredients：
300 grams (0.66 lb) beef
5 grams (1 tsp) black bean sauce
5 grams (1/6 oz) garlic mashed
5 grams (1/6 oz) ginger chopped
15 grams (1/2 oz) scallions sectioned
100 grams (7 tbsp) cooking oil
20 grams (1 1/3 tbsp) cooking wine
25 grams (1 1/2 tbsp) water
10 grams (2 tsp) mixture of cornstarch and water
10 grams (1 1/2 tbsp) dry cornstarch
1 egg white
5 grams (1 1/4 tsp) pepper powder
3 grams (1/2 tsp) salt 2 grams (1/2 tsp) MSG

Directions：
1. Cut the beef into slices 5 cm (2 inches) long and 3 cm (1. 2 inches) wide. Add 1 g (1/6 tsp) of salt and the egg white and mix well until the mixture becomes sticky. Sprinkle on the dry cornstarch and mix well.

2. Heat the oil in a wok to 70-100℃ （160-210˚F）. Stir-fry the beef slices until they are done. Take out and drain off the oil.

3. Put the oil back in the pot and heat it. Put in the black bean sauce, mashed garlic, chopped ginger, sectioned scallions and quick-fry until a strong aroma is achieved. Add the cooking wine, water, salt, MSG and pepper powder. Put in the beef slices and use mixture of cornstarch and water to thicken the sauce. Sprinkle on the sesame oil and serve.

Features：Unusually white.
Taste：The meat is tender and delicious.

煎焖芋肉
Bee_____auce

蚝油牛肉

主料：牛肉 300 克

辅料：姜片 10 克、葱段 50 克、胡萝卜 50 克、青椒 50 克

调料：味精 5 克、料酒 10 克、蚝油 15 克、酱油 5 克、湿淀粉 10 克、干淀粉 10 克、油 100 克、鸡蛋清 1 只、清汤 25 克、盐 1 克

制作：①将牛肉切成 5 厘米长、3 厘米宽的薄片，然后放盐 1 克和鸡蛋清搅拌上劲，放干淀粉拌匀。胡萝卜切片。青椒切丝。

②将锅烧热放入油，烧至三成热时，投入牛肉片，滑炒至熟，倒入漏勺中沥油。

③锅放回炉上，倒入余油，放入姜片、葱段、煸出香味，放胡萝卜片，青椒丝，加蚝油、料酒、酱油、清汤、味精烧沸，倒入牛肉片，加湿淀粉勾芡，淋上麻油，出锅装盘。

特点：金黄而有光泽

口味：鲜嫩爽滑

Beef with Oyster Sauce

Ingredients：
300 grams (0.66 lb) beef
10 grams (1/3 oz) sliced ginger
50 grams (1 2/3 oz) scallions sectioned
50 grams (0.11 lb) carrots
50 grams (0.11 lb) green peppers
5 grams (1 1/4 tsp) MSG
10 grams (2 tsp) cooking wine
15 grams (3 tsp) oyster sauce
5 grams (1 tsp) soy sauce
10 grams (2 tsp) mixture of cornstarch and water
10 grams (1 1/2 tbsp) dry cornstarch
100 grams (7 tbsp) cooking oil
1 egg white
25 grams (1 1/2 tbsp) water
1 gram (1/6 tsp) salt
3 grams (3/5 tsp) sesame oil

Directions：
1. Cut the beef into thin slices 5 cm (2 inches) long and 3 cm (1.2 inches) wide. Add 1 g (1/6 tsp) of salt and the egg white and stir until mixture becomes sticky. Add the dry cornstarch and mix well. Cut the carrots and green pepper into similar slices.

2. Heat the oil in a wok to 50-70℃ (115-160°F) and add the beef slices to stir-fry until they are done. Take out and drain off the oil.

3. Put the oil back into the wok, add the ginger and scallions, and stir-fry until they produce an aroma. Put in the carrot and green pepper slices and add the oyster sauce, cooking wine, soy sauce, water and MSG. Then bring the mixture to a boil. Put in the beef slices, add the mixture of cornstarch and water to thicken the sauce, and sprinkle the sesame oil on top and serve.

Features：Shiny and yellowish in color.
Taste：Slippery and tender.

蚝油牛肉
Beef with Oyster Sauce

家乡牛肉

主料：牛里脊肉 300 克

辅料：荷兰豆 50 克、洋葱片 50 克、芹菜片 50 克、黑木耳 25 克

调料：姜片 10 克、蒜茸 5 克、油 150 克（实耗 50 克）、盐 3 克、清汤 50 克、湿淀粉 10 克、味精 2 克、鸡蛋清 1 只、干淀粉 10 克、料酒 10 克

制作：①牛肉切成 5 厘米长、3 厘米宽的薄片放在碗中，加盐 1 克搅拌上劲，放鸡蛋清、干淀粉拌匀待用。

②锅放在炉上，加油 100 克，烧至四成热时，放入牛肉片，划散至熟，倒入漏勺中沥油。

③原锅放回火炉上，加油 50 克，倒入姜片、蒜茸、炒出香味，下酒料，倒入荷兰豆、洋葱片、芹菜片、黑木耳，翻炒均匀，放清汤、味精、盐烧沸，倒入牛肉片，翻炒后加湿淀粉勾芡，出锅装盘。

特点：清香爽口，色彩绚丽

口味：鲜香浓郁

Home-style Beef

Ingredients:

300 grams (0.66 lb) beef tenderloin
50 grams (0.11 lb) snow peas
50 grams (0.11 lb) onions sliced
50 grams (0.11 lb) celery sliced
25 grams (5/6 oz) black fungus previously soaked in water
10 grams (1/3 oz) ginger sliced
5 grams (1/5 oz) mashed garlic
150 grams (11 tbsp) cooking oil (only 1/3 to be consumed)
3 grams (1/2 tsp) salt
50 grams (3 tbsp) water
10 grams (2 tsp) mixture of cornstarch and water
2 grams (1/2 tsp) MSG
1 egg white
10 grams (1 1/2 tbsp) dry cornstarch
10 grams (2 tsp) cooking wine

Directions:

1. Cut the beef into thin slices 5 cm (2 inches) long and 3 cm (1.2 inches) wide. Put in a bowl. Add 1 g (1/6 tsp) of salt and stir until mixture is sticky. Add the egg white and dry cornstarch, and mix well.

2. Heat the oil in a wok to 70-100℃ (160-210°F) and put in the beef slices. Stir until the slices are done. Take out and drain off the oil.

3. Put 50 g (3 1/2 tbsp) of oil back into the wok. Add the ginger and scallions, and stir-fry until a strong aroma is produced. Put in the cooking wine, snow peas, onion slices, celery slices, and black fungus and stir well. Add the water, MSG and salt, and bring to boil. Add the beef, stir a few times and add the mixture of cornstarch and water. Take out and put on a plate to serve.

Features: Refreshing and tasty, it also looks beautiful.
Taste: Richly flavored and refreshingly delicious.

家乡牛肉
Home-style Beef

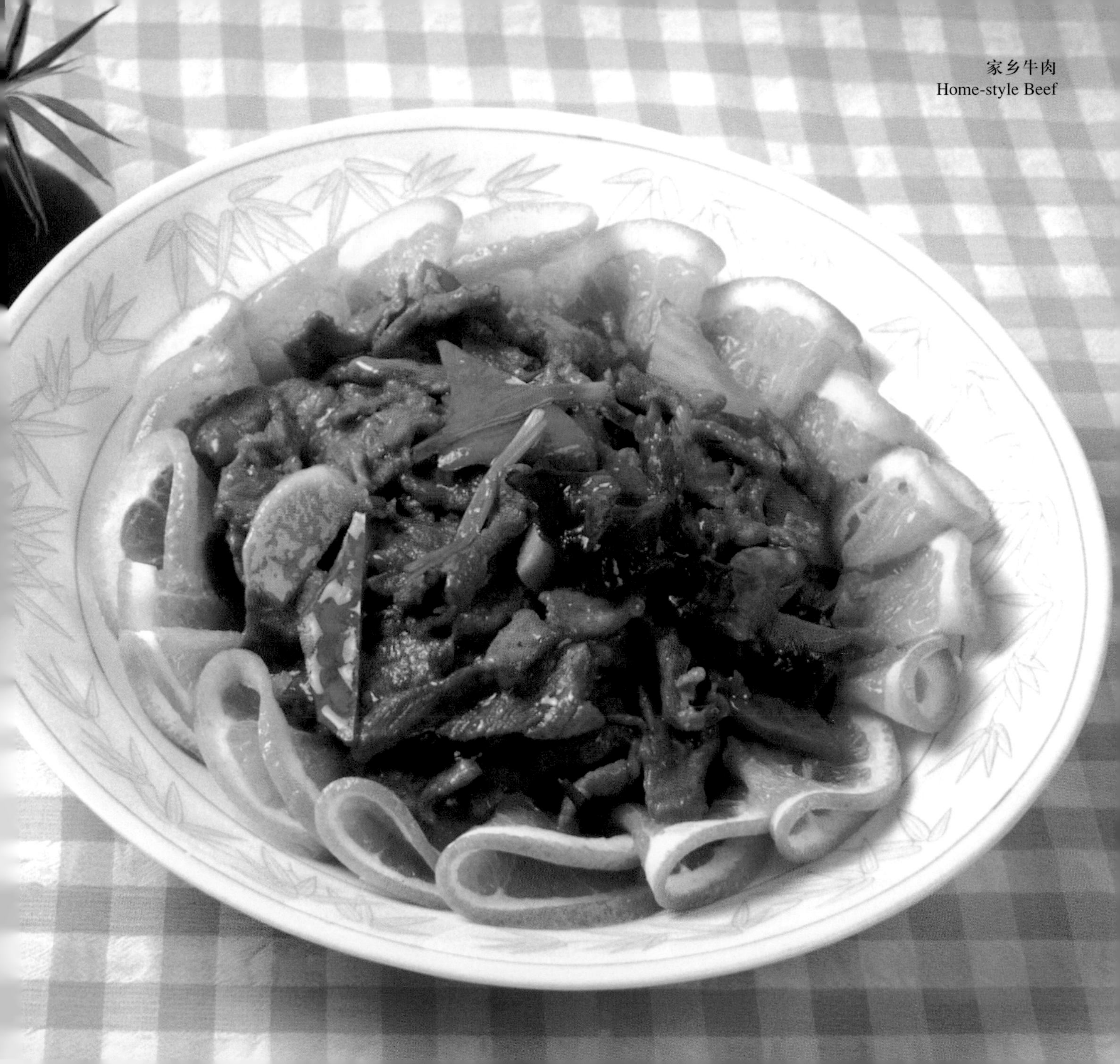

红焖牛肉

主料：牛腿肉 500 克

辅料：青蒜 50 克、洋葱 50 克

调料：葱 10 克、姜 2 克、大料 2 粒、料酒 25 克、酱油 50 克、味精 2 克、白糖 15 克、清汤 300 克、油 100 克、麻油 10 克、盐 3 克

制作：①将牛肉切成 3.5 厘米见方的块洗净，然后用开水煮至断生，捞出用清水洗净。

②青蒜切丝，姜切片，葱切段，洋葱切片。

③炒锅烧热加入油，烧至六成热时，投入葱段、姜片炒出香味，放入牛肉块炒透，加料酒、酱油、白糖、大料炒至上色入味，加清汤、味精烧沸，转小火焖 1 小时至牛肉酥烂，再转旺火，收干汤汁，淋入麻油，撒上青蒜丝，出锅装盘。

特点：牛肉酥烂, 卤汁稠浓

口味：咸中带甜

Braised Beef with Soy Sauce

Ingredients：

500 grams (1.1 lb) beef leg
50 grams (0.11 lb) leeks
50 grams (0.11 lb) onions
10 grams (1/3 oz) scallions
2 grams (1/15 oz) ginger
2 star anise
25 grams (1 2/3 tbsp) cooking wine
50 grams (2 2/3 tbsp) soy sauce
2 grams (1/2 tsp) MSG
15 grams (3 tsp) sugar
300 grams (3/5 cup) water
100 grams (7 tbsp) cooking oil
10 grams (2 tsp) sesame oil
3 grams (1/2 tsp) salt

Directions：

1. Cut the beef into cubes 3.5 cm (1.4 inches) long each side. Quick boil, take out and wash clean.

2. Cut the leeks into shreds, ginger into slices and scallions into sections.

3. Heat the oil in a wok to 135-170℃ (275-340°F) and stir-fry the scallions and ginger until they produce a distinctive aroma. Add the beef cubes and stir-fry well. Add the cooking wine, soy sauce, sugar and star anise, and stir-fry until the meat changes color. Add the water and MSG, and bring to boiling point. Turn to low fire to stew for 1 hour until the beef becomes soft. Use a high fire to boil off some of the soup. Sprinkle on the sesame oil, leek shreds and take out to serve.

Features：The beef is soft and the gravy is rich.
Taste：Salty with a slight sweet taste.

红焖牛肉
Braised Beef with Soy Sance

仔姜牛肉丝

主料：牛里脊肉 300 克

辅料：嫩姜 75 克

调料：鸡蛋清 1 只、盐 2 克、料酒 10 克、酱油 10 克、白糖 1 克、味精 1 克、湿淀粉 10 克、香醋 5 克、油 75 克、干淀粉 10 克、清汤 25 克

制作：①牛里脊肉洗净，切成长 6 厘米、宽和厚约 0.3 厘米的丝，加盐 1 克、鸡蛋清、干淀粉搅拌上浆待用。

②嫩姜切成与牛肉丝相仿的丝。

③炒锅烧热倒入油 50 克，烧至五成热时，下牛肉丝滑炒至熟，倒入漏勺中沥油。

④原锅倒入 25 克油，烧至五成热时，下嫩姜丝煸炒出香味，倒入肉丝、料酒、酱油、盐、糖、味精、清汤烧沸，用湿淀粉勾芡，再倒入香醋翻炒均匀，出锅装盘。

特点：肉丝鲜嫩，仔姜清香

口味：爽滑清口

Shredded Beef with Fresh Ginger

Ingredients:

300 grams (0.66 lb) beef tenderloin

75 grams (0.165 lb) fresh ginger

1 egg white

2 grams (1/3 tsp) salt

10 grams (2 tsp) cooking wine

10 grams (1 1/2 tsp) soy sauce

1 gram (1/4 tsp) sugar

10 grams (2 tsp) mixture of cornstarch and water

5 grams (1 tsp) vinegar

75 grams (5 tbsp) cooking oil

10 grams (1 1/2 tbsp) dry cornstarch

25 grams (1 2/3 tbsp) water

Directions:

1. Cut the beef into shreds 6 cm (1.6 inches) long and 0.3 cm (0.12 inch) thick and wide. Add 1 g (1/6 tsp) of salt, the egg white and dry cornstarch, and mix well.

2. Cut the ginger into shreds to the size similar to the beef.

3. Heat 50 g (3 1/2 tbsp) of the oil in a wok to 110-135℃ (230-275°F) and stir-fry the ginger shreds until they produce a strong aroma. Add the beef shreds, cooking wine, soy sauce, salt, sugar, MSG and water and bring to boiling point. Use the mixture of cornstarch and water to thicken the soup. Add the vinegar and turn several times. Take out to serve.

Features: The beef shreds are tender and the ginger adds a refreshing touch.

Taste: Succulent and soothing.

仔姜牛肉丝
Shredded Beef with Fresh Ginger

芝麻牛排

主料：牛里脊肉 300 克

辅料：白芝麻 50 克

调料：鸡蛋 1 只、料酒 10 克、盐 2 克、味精 1 克、面粉 20 克、油 250 克

制作：①将牛肉洗净切成 10 厘米见方、0.7 厘米厚的片,用刀拍松放入碗中,加料酒、盐、味精腌渍 10 分钟。

②鸡蛋磕入碗中,打散,将腌好的牛排裹上面粉并在鸡蛋液里托一下,然后均匀地粘上白芝麻待用。

③炒锅烧热加入油,烧至六成热时,逐个将牛排炸熟,倒出沥油。

④将炸好的牛排改刀切成 5 厘米见方的小块装盘即可。

特点：色泽金黄

口味：牛排鲜嫩,芝麻香脆

Beef Fillet with Sesame

Ingredients：
300 grams (0.66 lb) beef tenderloin
50 grams (0.11 lb) white sesame
1 egg
10 grams (2 tsp) cooking wine
2 grams (1/3 tsp) salt
1 gram (1/4 tsp) MSG
20 grams (2/3 oz) wheat flour
250 grams (1/2 cup) cooking oil

Directions：

1. Cut the beef into chunks 10 cm (4 inches) long and wide and 0.7 cm (0.28 inch) thick. Pat the beef with the side of a chopper to soften it. Place in a bowl. Add the cooking wine, salt and MSG, and marinate for 10 minutes.

2. Whip the egg in a bowl. Dust the marinated beef fillet with the wheat flour and then quickly dip in the whipped egg. Evenly sprinkle the sesame on the beef fillet.

3. Heat the oil in a wok to 135-170℃ (275-340˚F) and deep-fry the beef fillet chunks one by one until each is well done. Take out and drain off the oil.

4. Cut the deep-fried beef fillet into squares 5 cm (2 inches) long each side. Place on a plate and serve.

Features：Golden in color.

Taste：The fillet is tender and the sesame is crispy and aromatic.

芝麻牛排
Beef Fillet with Seasame

香酥牛肉卷

主料：牛肉末 300 克

辅料：面包屑 350 克

调料：鸡蛋 2 只、味精 1 克、盐 2 克、料酒 10 克、葱、姜末各 5 克、干淀粉 10 克、油 300 克

制作：①牛肉末加盐、味清、料酒、葱姜末、干淀粉 5 克搅拌上浆待用。

②鸡蛋磕入碗内打成蛋液。

③将浆好的牛肉末分成 3 份搓成直径 5 厘米、长 15 厘米的条状放入盘中上笼旺火蒸熟取出，冷却后均匀地裹上蛋液再粘上面包屑待用。

④炒锅烧热加入油，烧至五成热时，投入牛肉卷炸至外表呈金黄色倒出沥油。

⑤将牛肉卷切成 3 厘米长的斜刀块装盘。

特点：色泽金黄

口味：外酥里嫩，香味浓郁

Crispy Beef Roll

Ingredients:

300 grams (0.66 lb) ground beef
350 grams (0.77 lb) bread crumbs
2 eggs
1 gram (1/4 tsp) MSG
2 grams (1/3 tsp) salt
10 grams (2 tsp) cooking wine
5 grams (1/6 oz) finely cut scallions
5 grams (1/6 oz) chopped ginger
10 grams (1 1/2 tbsp) dry cornstarch
300 grams (3/5 cup) cooking oil

Directions:

1. Add to the ground beef the salt, MSG, cooking wine, scallions, ginger and 5 g (1 tbsp) of the dry cornstarch, and mix well until it becmes sticky.

2. Whip the eggs in a bowl.

3. Divide the ground beef into 3 portions and shape into long rolls 5 cm (2 inches) in diameter and 15 cm (6 inches) in length. Steam over strong fire for 10 minutes. When the rolls cool off, cover them with the whipped egg and bread crumbs.

4. Heat the oil in a wok to 110-135℃ (230-275°F) and deep-fry the beef rolls until they are a golden color. Drain off the oil.

5. Cut in a slanting way to divide the rolls into sections 3 cm (1.2 inches) long each. Put on a plate and serve.

Features: Golden in color.
Taste: Crispy outside and tender inside, the rolls are really delicious.

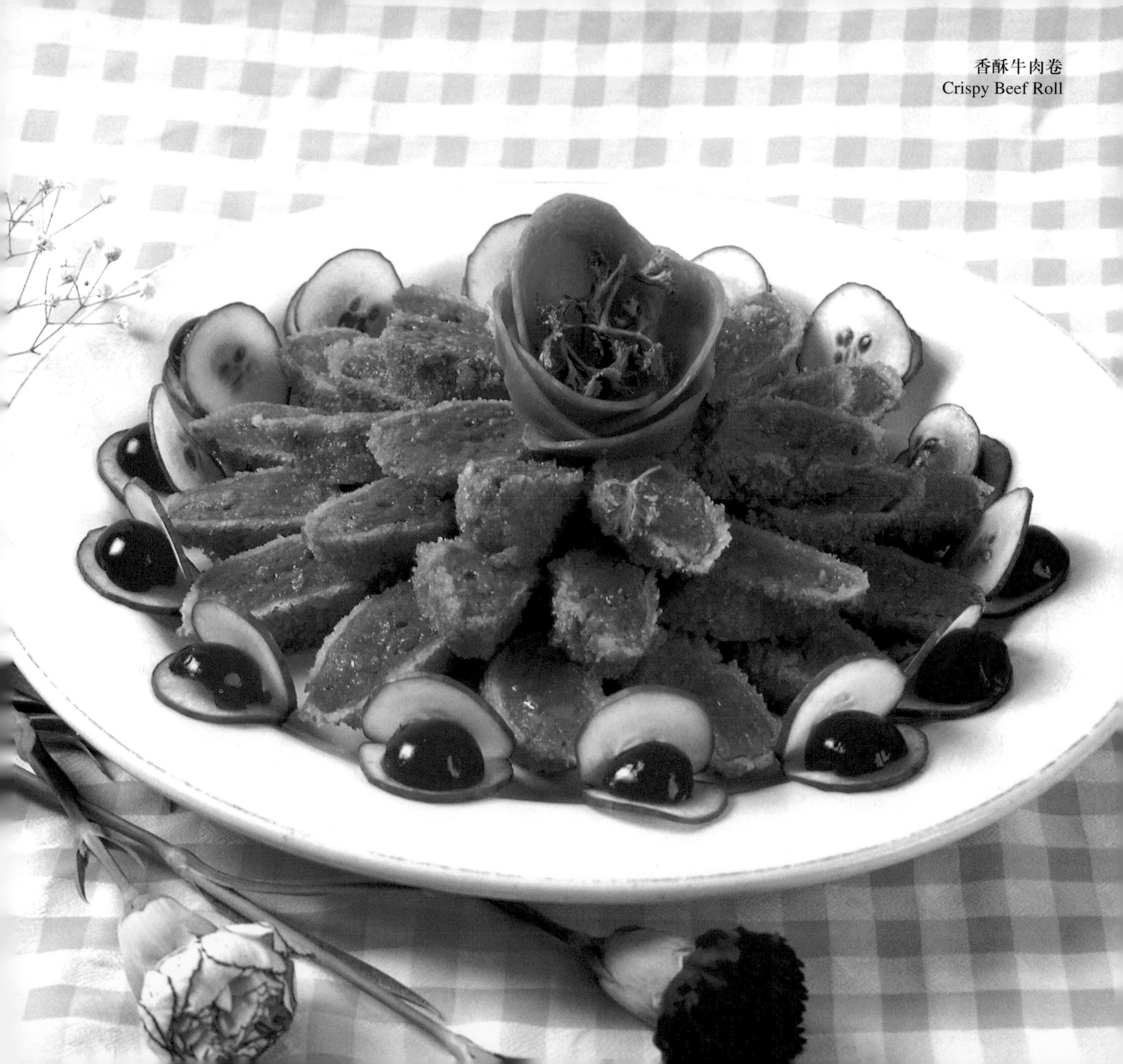

香酥牛肉卷
Crispy Beef Roll

菠萝牛肉

主料:牛里脊肉 300 克

辅料:罐装菠萝 75 克

调料:鸡蛋清 1 只、盐 2 克、清汤 30 克、干淀粉 10 克、湿淀粉 10 克、料酒 5 克、油 100 克、蒜茸 5 克

制作:①将牛肉切成 6 厘米长、3 厘米宽、0.3 厘米厚的片,加盐 1 克和干淀粉、鸡蛋清搅拌上浆备用。

②菠萝切成与肉片相仿的片。

③炒锅烧热加入油,烧至五成热时,投入牛肉片滑炒至熟,倒出沥油。

④原锅加油 20 克,放入蒜茸爆出香味,然后下菠萝片炒一下加清汤煮沸,加盐、味精、料酒,倒入牛肉片翻炒,用湿淀粉勾芡,出锅装盘。

特点:菠萝香味浓郁,牛肉滑嫩

口味:咸中带鲜,略带酸甜

Sliced Beef with Pineapple

Ingredients:

300 grams (0.66 lb) beef tenderloin
75 grams (0.165 lb) canned pineapple
1 egg white
2 grams (1/3 tsp) salt
30 grams (2 tbsp) water
10 grams (1 1/2 tbsp) dry cornstarch
10 grams (2 tsp) mixture of cornstarch and water
5 grams (1 tsp) cooking wine
100 grams (7 tbsp) cooking oil
5 grams (1 tsp) mashed garlic

Directions:

1. Cut the beef into slices 6 cm (2.4 inches) long, 3 cm (1.2 inches) wide and 0.3 cm (0.12 inch) thick. Add 1 g (1/6 tsp) of salt, dry cornstarch and egg white, and mix well.

2. Cut the pineapple into slices of a size similar to that of the beef.

3. Heat the oil to 110-135℃ (230-275°F) and stir-fry the beef slices until they are done. Take out and drain off the oil.

4. Keep 20 g (1 2/3 tbsp) of oil in the wok and stir-fry the mashed garlic until it produces a strong aroma. Put in the pineapple and quick stir-fry. Then add the water and bring to a boiling point. Add the salt, MSG, cooking wine and sliced beef. Turn over several times, thicken the dish with the mixture of cornstarch and water. Take out and serve.

Features: The pineapple produces a strong inviting flavor and the sliced beef is slippery.

Taste: Salty, refreshing with a slightly sweet and sour taste.

菠萝牛肉
Sliced Beef with Pineapple

脆皮牛肉

主料:牛里脊肉 300 克

辅料:面粉 100 克

调料:鸡蛋清 1 只、葱、姜末各 5 克、胡椒粉 0.5 克、苏打粉 0.5 克、料酒 10 克、盐 1 克、味精 1 克、香菜 50 克、油 200 克

制作:①将牛肉切成 5 厘米长、4 厘米宽、0.3 厘米的片,放碗中加葱姜末、料酒、苏打粉、盐、味精腌 10 分钟。香菜切 2 厘米长的段。

②将腌好的牛肉片加鸡蛋清拌匀,再将每片均匀地粘上面粉待用。

③炒锅烧热加入油,烧至七成热时,下肉片炸至金黄色倒出沥油,装盘。

④趁肉片热时撒上胡椒粉和香菜段即可。

特点:色泽金黄

口味:香酥咸鲜

Deep-fried Crispy Beef

Ingredients:
300 grams (0.66 lb) beef tenderloin
100 grams (0.22 lb) wheat flour
1 egg white
5 grams (1/6 oz) finely cut scallions
5 grams (1/6 oz) chopped ginger
1/2 gram (1/10 tsp) pepper powder
1/2 gram (1/10 tsp) soda ash
10 grams (2 tsp) cooking wine
1 gram (1/6 tsp) salt
1 gram (1/4 tsp) MSG
50 grams (0.11 lb) coriander
200 grams (2/5 cup) cooking oil

Directions:
1. Cut the beef into slices 5 cm (2 inches) long, 4 cm (1.6 inches) wide and 0.3 cm (0.12 inch) thick. Put the scallions, ginger, cooking wine, soda ash, salt and MSG in a bowl to marinate the sliced beef for 10 minutes. Cut the coriander into sections 2 cm (0.8 inch) long.

2. Mix evenly the egg white with the marinated beef and make sure each slice is dusted with flour.

3. Heat the oil in a wok to 180-200℃ (355-390°F) and deep-fry the beef slices until they are golden yellow in color. Take out, drain off the oil and place in a serving plate.

4. Sprinkle on the pepper powder and coriander while the beef is still hot.

Features: Golden yellow in color.
Taste: Crispy with a delicious and salty flavor.

脆皮牛肉
Deep-fried Crispy Beef

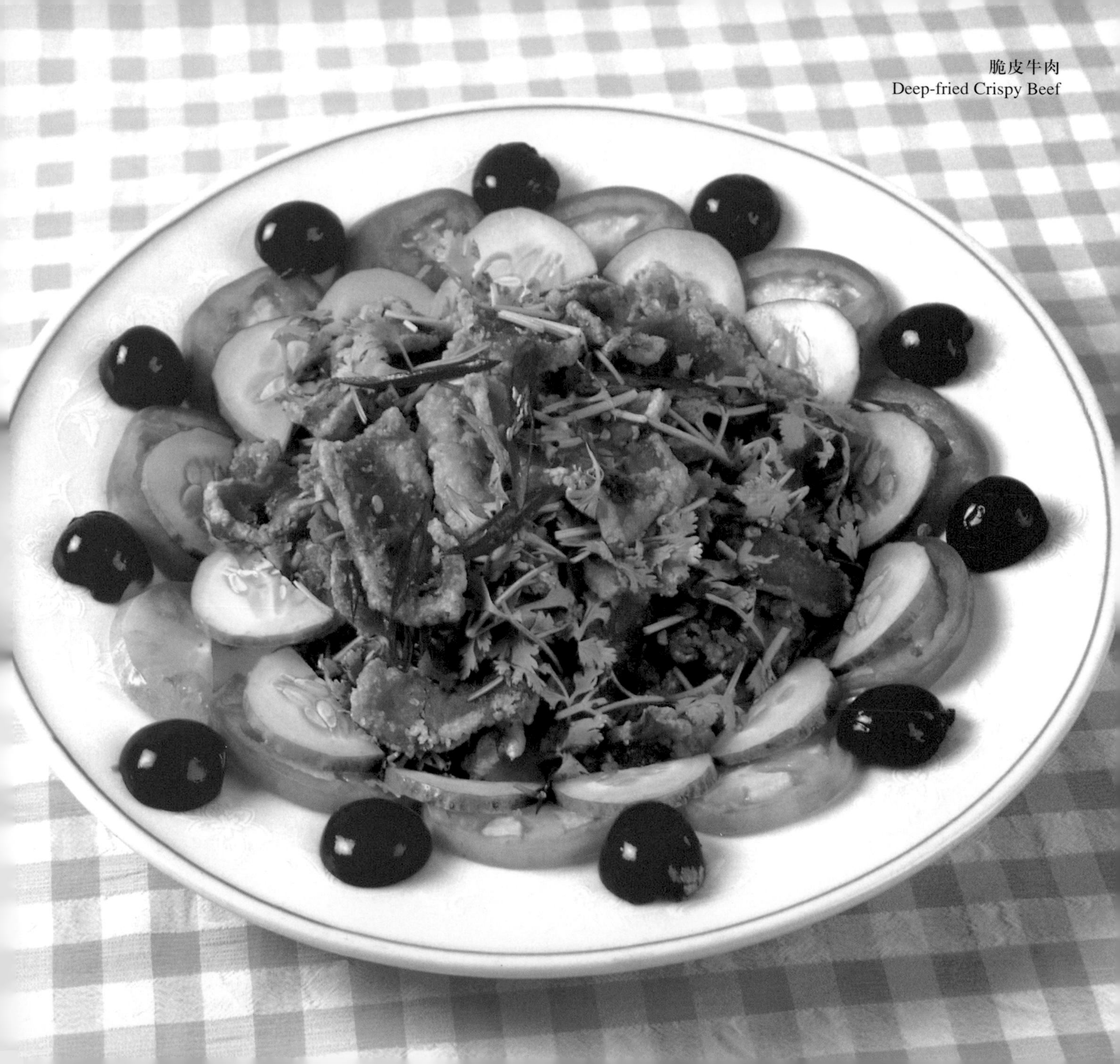

葱爆羊肉片

主料:羊肉 400 克

辅料:大葱 150 克

调料:鸡蛋清 1 只、盐 2 克、味精 1 克、料酒 5 克、酱油 5 克、油 100 克、湿淀粉 10 克、干淀粉 10 克、清汤 50 克

制作:①羊肉切成 5 厘米长、3 厘米宽的薄片放在碗中,加盐 1 克加鸡蛋清搅拌上劲,加干淀粉拌匀待用。大葱切成象眼片。

②把锅放在炉上烧热,加油 100 克,烧至四成热时,投入羊肉片滑炒至熟,倒入漏勺中沥油。

③把锅放回炉上,倒入油 20 克烧热,放入大葱片煸出香味,依次放入料酒、酱油、清汤烧沸,再放入盐、味精,倒入羊肉片,迅速翻炒,用湿淀粉勾芡,出锅装盘即可。

特点:油润光亮,肉白葱绿

口味:羊肉滑嫩,大葱鲜香

Mutton Slices with Scallions

Ingredients:

400 grams (0.88 lb) mutton or lamb
150 grams (0.33 lb) scallions
1 egg white
2 grams (1/3 tsp) salt
1 gram (1/4 tsp) MSG
5 grams (1 tsp) cooking wine
5 grams (1 tsp) soy sauce
100 grams (7 tbsp) cooking oil
10 grams (2 tsp) mixture of cornstarch and water
10 grams (1 1/2 tbsp) dry cornstarch
50 grams (3 tbsp) water

Directions:

1. Cut the mutton or lamb into thin slices 5 cm (2 inches) long and 3 cm (1.2 inches) wide. Put in a bowl. Add 1 g (1/6 tsp) of salt and stir until the mixture becomes sticky. Add the egg white and dry cornstarch and mix well. Slice the onions.

2. Heat the oil in a wok to 70-100℃ (160-210°F) and slippery-fry the mutton slices until they are done. Take out and drain off the oil.

3. Put back 20 g (1 1/2 tbsp) of oil into the wok and stir-fry the scallions until they produce a strong aroma. Add in the cooking wine, soy sauce, and water and bring to boiling point. Add the salt and MSG, and put in the mutton. Quickly stir several times and then thicken the sauce with the mixture of cornstarch and water. Take out and serve.

Features: Shiny and beautifully colored with white meat and green scallions.

Taste: The mutton is slippery and tender and the scallions are aromatic.

葱爆羊肉片
Mutton Slices with Scallions

红烧狮子头

主料：猪五花肉 500 克

调料：酱油 175 克、料酒 100 克、干淀粉 150 克、葱末、姜末各 50 克、清汤 300 克、盐 3 克、味精 2 克、糖 10 克、鸡蛋 1 只、油 250 克（实耗 150 克）

制作：①猪五花肉剁成肉末，加葱末、姜末各 40 克、料酒 50 克、酱油 50 克、盐 2 克、味精 1 克，搅拌上劲，磕入鸡蛋，加干淀粉拌匀。

②把肉末分成 8 份，再搓成肉圆，制成狮子头生坯。

③把锅烧热，倒入油，烧至八成热时，放入狮子头生坯，炸至金黄色，倒入漏勺中沥油。

④把锅放回炉上，倒入油 80 克，待油温升至四成热时，投入余下的葱、姜末炒出香味，放入狮子头和余下的料酒、酱油、糖、盐、味精、清汤用大火煮开，转小火焖熟，待汤汁收浓时出锅装盘。

特点：色泽红亮

口味：咸鲜带甜

Stewed Large Pork Balls with Brown Sauce

Ingredients：

500 grams (1.1 lb) streaky pork
175 grams (9 1/2 tbsp) soy sauce
100 grams (7 tbsp) cooking wine
150 grams (12 tbsp) dry cornstarch
50 grams (1 2/3 oz) chopped ginger
50 grams (12/3 oz) finely cut scallions
300 grams (3/5 cup) water
3 grams (1/2 tsp) salt
2 grams (1/2 tsp) MSG
10 grams (2 tsp) sugar
1 egg
250 grams (1/2 cup) oil (150 g or 11 tbsp to be consumed)

Directions：

1. Make minced meat with the pork. Add 40 g (1 /13 oz) each of the finely cut scallions and chopped ginger, 50 g (3 1/2 tbsp) of the cooking wine, 50 g (2 2/3 tbsp) of soy sauce, 2 g (1/2 tsp) of salt, and 1 g (1/4 tsp) MSG and stir until mixture becomes sticky. Then add the egg and dry cornstarch and mix well.

2. Divide the minced meat into 8 portions and roll into 8 balls.

3. Heat the oil in a wok to 200-22-℃ (390-430˚F) and deep-fry the meatballs into a golden yellow color. Take out and drain off oil.

4. Put 80 g (5 tbsp) of the oil back into the wok and heat it to 70-100℃ (160-210˚F). Put the remaining scallions and ginger into the wok and stir-fry until they produce a strong aroma. Add the deep-fried meatballs and the remaining cooking wine, soy sauce, sugar, salt, MSG and water and cook over high fire to bring it to boiling point. Turn to a low fire to simmer and when the sauce thickens, take out and serve.

Features：Shiny, with a dark brown color.
Taste：Salty, slightly sweet and delicious.

红烧狮子头
Stewed Large Pork Balls with Brown Sauce

滑溜里脊

主料：猪里脊肉 400 克

调料：盐 2 克、味精 1 克、葱、姜末各 5 克、料酒 5 克、油 300 克(实耗 50 克)、鸡蛋清 1 只、干淀粉 10 克

制作：①猪里脊切成长 6 厘米、宽和厚约 0.3 厘米的丝，放在碗中，加盐 1 克和鸡蛋清搅拌上劲，加干淀粉拌匀。

②把锅放火上烧热，放入油，烧至四成热时，放入肉丝划散，待肉丝色变白即倒入漏勺中沥油。

③锅放回炉上放入油 25 克烧热，投入葱、姜末煸出香味，加料酒、盐、味精，倒入肉丝，翻炒均匀，出锅装盘即可。

特点：色白润泽

口味：滑嫩爽口

Slippery-fried Pork Tenderloin

Ingredients：
400 grams (0.88 lb) pork tenderloin
2 grams (1/3 tsp) salt
1 gram (1/4 tsp) MSG
5 grams (1/6 oz) finely cut scallions
5 grams (1/6 oz) chopped ginger
5 grams (1 tsp) cooking wine
300 grams (3/5 cup) cooking oil (only 1/6 to be consumed)
1 egg white
10 grams (1 1/2 tbsp) dry cornstarch

Directions：
1. Cut the pork tenderloin into shreds 6 cm (2.4 inches) long, 0.3 cm (0.12 inch) thick and wide. Put in a bowl, add 1 g (1/6 tsp) of salt and the egg white. Stir until mixture becomes elastic. Add the dry cornstarch and mix well.

2. Heat the oil in a wok to 70-100℃ (160-210˚F). Put in the shredded pork and stir. Once the meat turns white in color, take out and drain off the oil.

3. Put 25 g (1 1/2 tbsp) of the oil in the wok, add the scallions and ginger and heat until they produce a strong aroma. Put in the cooking wine, salt and MSG. Add the pork shreds and stir to mix well. Take out and serve.

Features：Beautiful white color and looks nicely shiny.
Taste：Tender and succulent.

滑溜里脊
Slippery-fried Pork Tenderlion

咸蛋蒸肉饼

主料：瘦猪肉末 350 克

辅料：生咸鸭蛋 3 只

调料：干淀粉 5 克、酱油 5 克、味精 1 克、糖 5 克、油 10 克、葱、姜末各 5 克

制作：①将生咸鸭蛋打碎,蛋黄与蛋白分别倒入两碗内待用。

②猪肉末内放咸蛋白、酱油、糖、味精、葱姜末搅拌上劲,再放干淀粉拌匀,放在盘内铺平,将蛋黄倒在上面,然后淋上油,做成生坯。

③将咸蛋肉饼生坯放入笼屉内,旺火蒸 15 分钟即可。

特点：色彩鲜明

口味：咸鲜适中

Steamed Pork with Salted Eggs

Ingredients：
350 grams (0.77 lb) lean minced pork
3 raw salted duck eggs
5 grams (1 tbsp) dry cornstarch
5 grams (1 tsp) soy sauce
1 gram (1/4 tsp) MSG
5 grams (1 tsp) sugar
10 grams (2 tsp) cooking oil
5 grams (1/6 oz) finely cut scallions
5 grams (1/6 oz) chopped ginger

Directions：
1. Break the eggs and separate the egg white and yolk into two bowls.

2. Add the minced pork to the salted egg white, as well as the soy sauce, sugar, MSG, ginger and scallions. Stir until the mixture becomes sticky. Mix well with the dry cornstarch. Evenly spread out on a plate and pour the egg yolk on top. Sprinkle on the cooking oil and roll and shape the mixture into one big cake.

3. Steam over a high fire for 15 minutes and it is ready to serve.

Features：Sharp contrast of the colors of the ingredients.
Taste：Salty to the right taste.

咸蛋蒸肉饼
Steamed Pork with Salted Eggs

冬笋肉丝

主料: 猪里脊肉 250 克

辅料: 冬笋 150 克

调料: 盐 3 克、白糖 3 克、料酒 10 克、味精 1 克、鸡蛋清 1 只、干淀粉 10 克、湿淀粉 10 克、油 100 克、清汤 50 克、葱、姜末各 5 克

制作: ①猪肉洗净,切成长 6 厘米、宽和厚约 0.3 厘米的丝。冬笋切成同样粗细的丝。

②肉丝放碗中,加盐 1 克和鸡蛋清搅拌上劲、加干淀粉拌匀待用。

③把锅放在炉上烧热,加油 100 克,烧至四成热时,投入肉丝划散至熟,倒出沥油。

④原锅放回炉上,倒入油烧热,投入冬笋丝炒熟,加葱姜末、料酒、清汤烧沸,加盐、味精、白糖投入肉丝,用湿淀粉勾芡,翻炒均匀,出锅装盘。

特点: 肉丝鲜嫩,笋丝鲜脆

口味: 咸鲜

Shredded Pork with Winter Bamboo Shoots

Ingredients:

250 grams (0.55 lb) pork tenderloin
150 grams (0.33 lb) winter bamboo shoots
3 grams (1/2 tsp) salt
3 grams (3/5 tsp) sugar
10 grams (2 tsp) cooking wine
1 gram (1/4 tsp) MSG
1 egg white
10 grams (1 1/2 tbsp) dry cornstarch
10 grams (2 tsp) mixture of cornstarch and water
100 grams (7 tbsp) cooking oil
50 grams (3 tbsp) water
5 grams (1/6 oz) finely cut scallions
5 grams (1/6 oz) chopped ginger

Directions:

1. Cut the pork into strips 6 cm (2.4 inches) long and 0.3 cm (0.12 inch) thick and wide. Cut the winter bamboo shoots into the same sized strips.

2. Put the meat strips into a bowl. Add 1 g (1/6 tsp) of salt and stir until mixture becomes elastic. Add the egg white and dry cornstarch and mix well.

3. Heat the oil in a wok until it reaches 70-100℃ (160-210°F) and stir-fry the pork strips until they are done. Take out and drain off the oil.

4. Put 20 g (1 1/2 tbsp) of the oil back into the wok, throw in the bamboo shoots and stir-fry until they are done. Add the scallions, ginger, cooking wine, and water and bring to a boiling point. Add the salt, MSG and sugar before putting in the pork. Use the mixture of cornstarch and water to thicken the sauce. Mix well and put on a plate to serve.

Features: The pork shreds are really tender and the bamboo shoots are crispy.

Taste: Salty and delicious.

冬笋肉丝
Shredded Pork with Winter Bamboo Shoots

梅干菜扣肉

主料:带皮猪肋条肉 500 克

辅料:梅干菜 75 克

调料:料酒 10 克、白糖 50 克、味精 2 克、酱油 100 克、盐 2 克、葱、姜各 5 克、清汤 500 克

制作:①猪肉刮洗干净。梅干菜用水泡软洗净。葱、姜切片。

②猪肉放在汤锅中煮至断生,捞出用清水洗净,再入另一锅中加入酱油、料酒、白糖、清汤烧沸后撇去浮沫,加盖改用小火焖烧半小时,至肉色变红,汤汁粘稠时取出晾凉后切成 0.3 厘米厚的片待用。

③取中碗,碗底中放上薄薄一层梅干菜,把肉片皮朝下整齐排在碗里,中间放入梅干菜、盐、葱姜片。上笼用旺火蒸 2 小时至肉酥烂,梅干菜软糯取出。将碗中汤汁滗到另一碗中,然后翻扣在盘中,再将汤汁浇到肉上即可。

特点:肉质鲜嫩,梅干菜香糯

口味:肥而不腻,咸中带甜

Twice-cooked Pork with Preserved Vegetables

Ingredients:

500 grams (1.1 lb) pork filleted off the ribs with the skin on
75 grams (0.16 lb) preserved dry vegetables
10 grams (2 tsp) cooking wine
50 grams (0.11 lb) sugar
2 grams (1/2 tsp) MSG
100 grams (5 1/2 tbsp) soy sauce
2 grams (1/3 tsp) salt
5 grams (1/6 oz) scallions
5 grams (1/6 oz) ginger
500 grams (1 cup) water

Directions:

1. Clean the pork with the skin on. Soak the preserved dry vegetables. Cut the scallions and ginger into thin slices.

2. Boil the pork. Once it boils, take out the meat and wash it clean. Use another pot and put the pork into it along with soy sauce, cooking wine, sugar and water in it to boil. Skim off the foam once it starts to boil. Turn to low fire and cook for 30 minutes until the meat turns red and the soup becomes sticky. Take meat out and cool off. Cut the meat into slices 0.3 cm (0.12 inch) thick.

3. Use a large bowl and put in a thin layer of the dry vegetables. Neatly place the pork slices on top of the vegetables with the skin side down. Place more dry vegetables on top of this, as well as salt, scallions and ginger, and then place on another layer of the meat. Steam over strong fire for 2 hours until the meat is really soft. Carefully pour out the gravy into another bowl. Turn the bowl with the meat upside down onto a plate. Remove the bowl and pour the gravy from the other bowl on top of the meat and vegetables.

Features: The meat is soft and tender, while the dry vegetables are soft and fragrant.

Taste: Fat but not greasy. Salty with a slight sweet touch.

梅干菜扣肉
Twice-cooked Pork with Preserved Vegetable

京都金排骨

主料：猪肋排 500 克

调料：水 150 克、白糖 15 克、番茄酱 60 克、糖醋汁 25 克、盐 3 克、味精 5 克、料酒 25 克、鸡蛋液 1 只、干淀粉 75 克、油 500 克(实耗 150 克)

制作：①猪肋排洗净,切成长 6 厘米、宽 2 厘米的块,然后用盐 1.5 克、料酒 2.5 克、鸡蛋液、干淀粉拌匀。

②将糖醋汁、番茄酱,余下的盐、味精、白糖加水调成汁。

③炒锅放油,待油温烧至五成热时,放入猪肋排炸至金黄色,倒入漏勺中沥油。

④原锅倒入预先调成的汁烧沸,倒入料酒、排骨,转小火烧至汁干,出锅装盘

特点：色泽红润

口味：酸甜可口

Capital-style Pork Ribs

Ingredients:

500 grams (1.1 lb) pork ribs
150 grams (10 tbsp) water
15 grams (3 tsp) sugar
60 grams (5 1/4 tbsp) ketchup
25 grams (1 2/3 tbsp) sweet vinegar
3 grams (1/2 tsp) salt
5 grams (1 1/4 tsp) MSG
25 grams (1 1/3 tbsp) cooking wine
1 egg
75 grams (6 tbsp) dry cornstarch
500 grams (1 cup) cooking oil (only 3/10 to be consumed)

Directions:

1. Wash the pork ribs clean and cut them into chunks 6 cm (2.4 inches) long and 2 cm (0.8 inch) wide. Mix with half of the salt, 2 1/2 g (2/5 tsp) of the cooking wine, egg and dry cornstarch.

2. Make a sauce with the sweet vinegar, ketchup, the remaining salt, MSG, sugar and water.

3. Heat the oil in a wok to 110-135℃ (230-275°F) and deep-fry the pork ribs until they are golden brown in color. Take out and drain off the oil.

4. Put the pre-prepared sauce in the wok and bring to a boiling point. Add the cooking wine and pork ribs and put over a low fire to absorb the sauce.

Features: Beautifully colored in dark brown.
Taste: Sweet and sour to the right taste.

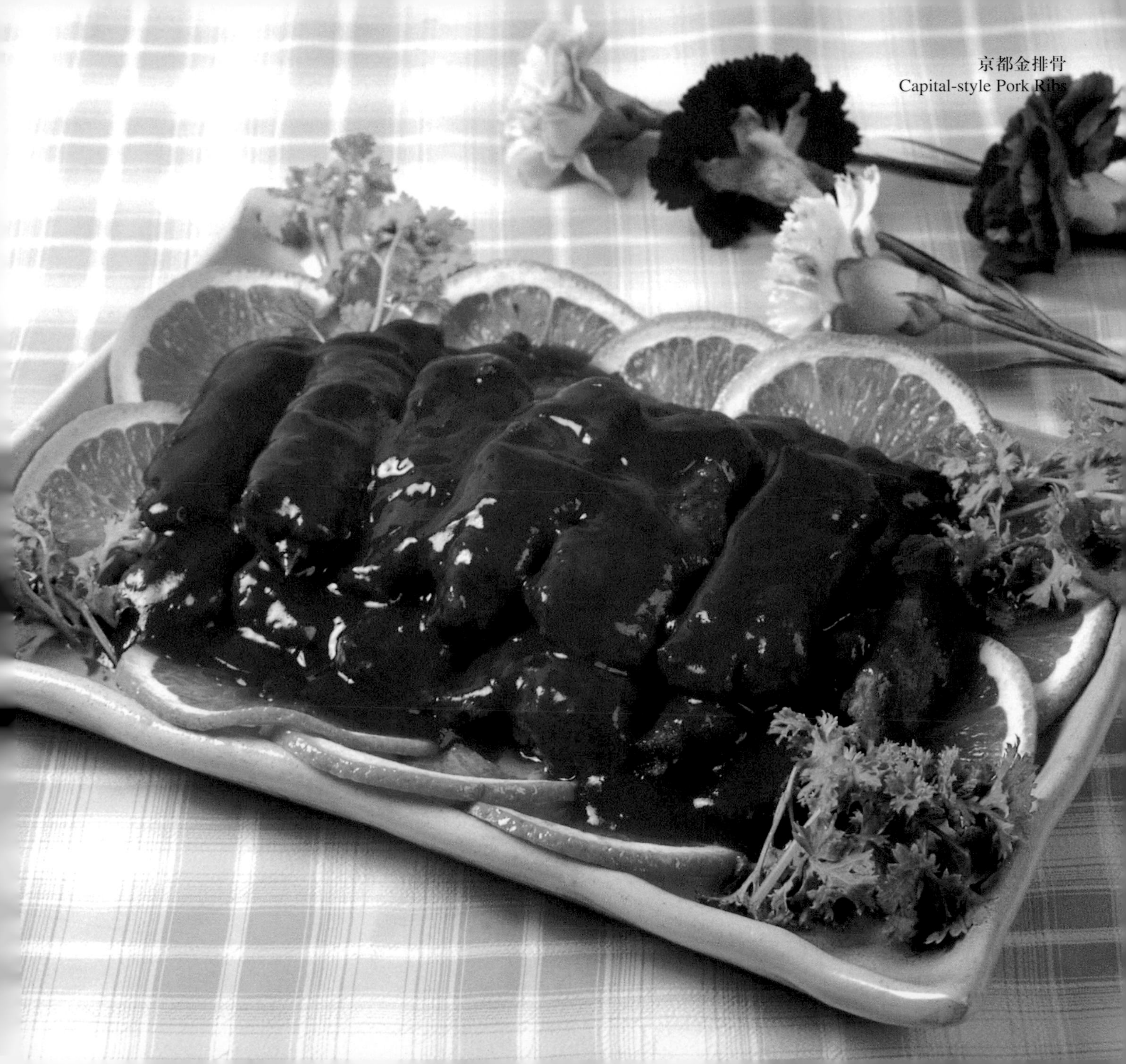

京都金排骨
Capital-style Pork Ribs

炒三丁

主料:猪里脊肉 250 克

辅料:胡萝卜 150 克、黄瓜 150 克

调料:酱油 15 克、盐 2 克、味精 1 克、料酒 10 克、葱、姜末各 5 克、清汤 15 克、油 100 克、干淀粉 5 克、湿淀粉 5 克、鸡蛋清 1 只

制作:①猪肉切成 0.8 厘米见方的丁,放入碗中,加盐 1 克搅拌上劲加干淀粉、鸡蛋清拌匀待用。胡萝卜、黄瓜都切成与肉丁大小相同的丁。

②炒锅放火上烧热,加油 50 克,烧至四成热时,放肉丁滑炒至熟,倒入漏勺中沥油。

③原锅放回炉上,放油 50 克烧热后,投入葱姜末,煸出香味,放入胡萝卜丁、黄瓜丁翻炒后放料酒、酱油、清汤烧沸,然后加盐、味精再投入肉丁,翻炒均匀,用湿淀粉勾芡,出锅装盘。

特点:色彩绚丽

口味:肉质滑嫩、清香

Triple Cubes

Ingredients:

250 grams (0.55 lb) pork tenderloin
150 grams (0.33 lb) carrots
150 grams (0.33 lb) cucumbers
15 grams (3 tsp) soy sauce
2 grams (1/3 tsp) salt
1 gram (1/4 tsp) MSG
10 grams (2 tsp) cooking wine
5 grams (1/6 oz) finely cut scallions
5 grams (1/6 oz) chopped ginger
15 grams (1 tbsp) water
100 grams (7 tbsp) cooking oil
5 grams (1 tbsp) dry cornstarch
5 grams (1 tsp) mixture of cornstarch and water
1 egg white

Directions:

1. Cut the pork into cubes 0.8 cm (0.3 inch) each side. Put in a bowl, add 1 g (1/6 tsp) of salt and stir until mixture becomes sticky. Add the dry cornstarch and egg white, and mix well. Cut the carrots and cucumbers into dices the same size as the pork.

2. Put 50 g (3 1/2 tbsp) of the cooking oil in a wok and heat to 70-100℃ (160-210°F). Put in the pork cubes and stir-fry until they are done. Take out and drain off the oil.

3. Put the remaining 50 g (3 1/2 tbsp) of oil in the wok and heat. Stir-fry the scallions and ginger until they produce a strong aroma. Add the carrot and cucumber dices and stir several times. Put in the cooking wine, soy sauce and water, and bring to boiling point. Add the remaining salt, MSG and pork, and evenly stir and mix. Add the mixture of cornstarch and water to thicken the sauce. Take out and serve.

Features: Beautiful combination of colors.
Taste: The meat is tender, slippery and delicious.

红烧排骨

主料:猪肋排 500 克

调料:葱段、姜片各 50 克、盐 3 克、料酒 25 克、味精 2 克、糖 50 克、酱油 100 克、油 250 克(实耗 100 克)、清汤 250 克

制作:①猪肋排斩成 6 厘米见方的块洗净,加盐 2 克,腌渍 10 分钟待用。

②炒锅放在炉上烧热,加油 250 克,烧至七成热时,投入肋排炸至断生,倒入漏勺中沥油。

③原锅加油 25 克烧热,投入葱段、姜片,炒出香味,依次放入肋排、料酒、酱油、清汤、盐、味精、糖烧沸后,转小火焖半小时左右,再转大火收干汤汁,出锅装盘。

特点:色泽红亮

口味:咸中带甜,肉质鲜嫩

Pork Ribs in Brown Sauce

Ingredients:
500 grams (1.1 lb) pork ribs
50 grams (0.11 lb) sectioned scallions
50 grams (0.11 lb) sliced ginger
3 grams (1/2 tsp) salt
25 grams (1 1/2 tbsp) cooking wine
2 grams (1/2 tsp) MSG
50 grams (0.11 lb) sugar
100 grams (6 tbsp) soy sauce
250 grams (1/2 cup) cooking oil (only 2/5 to be consumed)
250 grams (1/2 cup) water

Directions:
1. Cut the pork ribs into chunks 6 cm (2.4 inches) long and wash clean. Mix with 2 g (1/3 tsp) of salt and let marinate for 10 minutes.

2. Heat the oil in a wok to 180-200℃ (355-390°F) and quick deep-fry the ribs. Take out and drain off the oil.

3. Keep 25 g (1 2/3 tbsp) of oil in the wok and stir-fry the scallions and ginger until they produce a strong aroma. Put in the pork ribs, cooking wine, soy sauce, water, salt, MSG and sugar. Bring it to boiling point and turn to low fire to cook for 30 minutes. Use strong fire to reduce the amount of gravy. Take out to serve.

Features: Brightly shiny.
Taste: Salty with a sweet touch. The meat is tender and delicious.

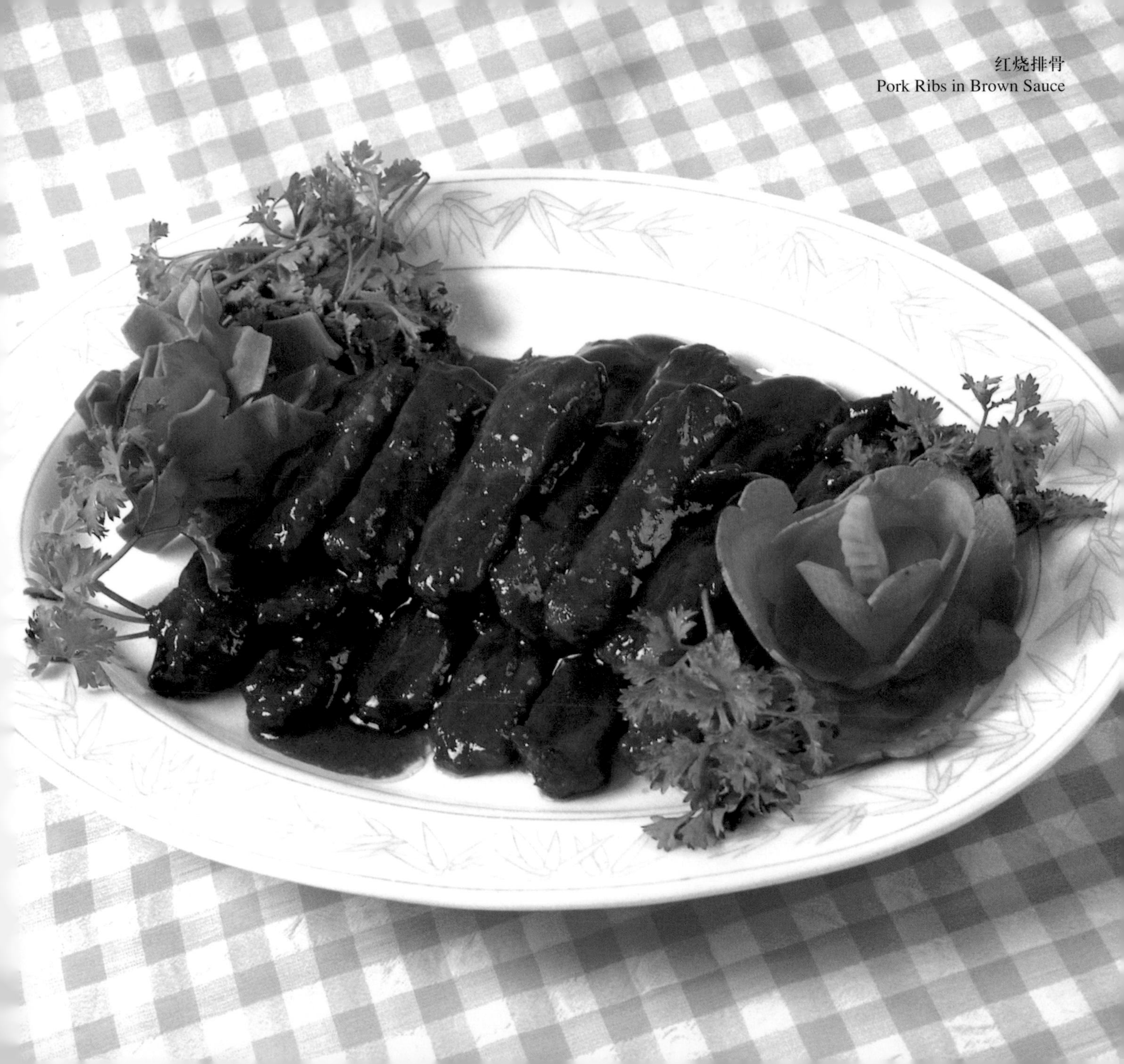

红烧排骨
Pork Ribs in Brown Sauce

回锅肉片

主料：带皮猪腿肉 250 克

辅料：大葱 150 克、芹菜 50 克

调料：甜面酱 10 克、料酒 10 克、豆瓣辣酱 25 克、酱油 5 克、白糖 5 克、油 25 克、干红辣椒 2 克

制作：①猪腿肉刮洗干净，放入锅中加水煮至皮软肉熟，捞出冷却。

②冷却后，将猪腿肉切成 5 厘米长、0.3 厘米厚、3 厘米宽的片。大葱剥去黄叶、根、须洗净，斜切成片。芹菜切成段。

③炒锅烧热，倒入油，烧至五成热时，下肉片，煸炒至肉片紧缩卷起，下干红辣椒、豆瓣辣酱，甜面酱、料酒、白糖、酱油、芹菜段翻炒均匀，上色后再投入大葱片翻炒几下，出锅装盘。

特点：色呈酱红

口味：鲜咸甜辣，香味扑鼻

Twice-cooked Pork with Spicy Sauce

Ingredients：

250 grams (0.55 lb) pork leg meat with the skin on
150 grams (0.33 lb) scallions
50 grams (0.11 lb) celery
10 grams (2 tsp) sweet soy bean paste
25 grams (1 tbsp) spicy bean paste
10 grams (2 tsp) cooking wine
5 grams (1 tsp) soy sauce
5 grams (1 tsp) sugar
25 grams (2 tbsp) cooking oil
2 grams (1/15 oz) dry red chili

Directions：

1. Boil the pork leg until the skin becomes soft and the meat is done. Take out and cool off.

2. Cut the meat into slices 5 cm (2 inches) long, 0.3 cm (0.12 inch) thick and 3 cm (1.2 inches) wide. Cut the scallions into slices. Cut the celery into sections 3 cm (1.2 inches) long.

3. Heat the oil to 110-135°C (230-275°F). Put in the pork slices and stir-fry until the slices roll up. Put in the red chili, spicy bean paste, sweet bean paste, cooking wine, sugar, soy sauce and celery, and stir well several times. When brown color shows on the meat and celery, add the scallions and keep stirring several more times. Put on a plate and serve.

Features：Dark brown in color.
Taste：Salty, sweet and spicy with a strong delicious aroma.

回锅肉片
Twice-cooked Pork with Spicy Sauce

青椒肉丝

主料：猪里脊肉 300 克

辅料：青椒 100 克

调料：盐 5 克、味精 1 克、干淀粉 10 克、湿淀粉 10 克、油 100 克、鸡蛋清 1 只、料酒 10 克、清汤 25 克

制作：①猪肉洗净切成长 6 厘米、宽厚皆约 0.3 厘米的丝放入碗中，加盐 1 克搅拌上劲，加鸡蛋清、干淀粉拌均匀。青椒去梗、籽洗净，切成与肉丝相同的细丝。

②炒锅烧热，加油烧至五成热时，放入肉丝滑炒至熟，倒入漏勺中沥油。

③原锅加油 25 克，投入青椒丝，稍加煸炒，投入肉丝，加料酒、盐、味精、清汤烧沸用湿淀粉勾芡，出锅装盘。

特点：肉色白中泛粉，青椒碧绿

口味：肉丝鲜嫩，青椒脆嫩，咸鲜可口

Shredded Pork with Green Peppers

Ingredients:

300 grams (0.66 lb) pork tenderloin
100 grams (0.22 lb) green peppers
5 grams (5/6 tsp) salt
1 gram (1/4 tsp) MSG
10 grams (1 1/2 tbsp) dry cornstarch
10 grams (2 tsp) mixture of cornstarch and water
100 grams (7 tbsp) cooking oil
1 egg white
10 grams (2 tsp) cooking wine
25 grams (1 1/2 tbsp) water

Directions:

1. Cut the meat into shreds 6 cm (2.4 inches) long and 0.3 cm (0.12 inch) thick and wide. Put in a bowl. Add 1 g (1/6 tsp) of salt and stir until mixture becomes sticky. Add the egg white and dry cornstarch and mix well. Cut the green peppers into shreds of similar size to the meat.

2. Heat the oil to 110-135℃ （230-275° F) and stir-fry the pork shreds until they are done. Take out and drain off the oil.

3. Put 25 g (1 2/3 tbsp) of oil in the wok and stir-fry the shredded green peppers for 1 minute. Add the shredded pork, cooking wine, salt, MSG and water, and bring to boiling point. Put in the mixture of cornstarch and water to thicken the sauce. Take out and serve.

Features: The meat is white with a light pink tinge, while the peppers are invitingly green.

Taste: The shredded pork is tender and the green peppers crispy. The dish is salty to the right taste.

青椒肉丝
Shredded Pork with Green Peppers

麻辣肉片

主料：猪里脊肉 250 克

调料：鸡蛋清 1 只、花椒 1 克、姜末 5 克、熟芝麻粉 10 克、味精 1 克、辣椒油 5 克、酱油 10 克、豆瓣酱 10 克、盐 1 克、白糖 10 克、干淀粉 5 克、湿淀粉 5 克、清汤 50 克、油 100 克

制作：①猪里脊肉洗净切 5 厘米长、3 厘米宽的片，放碗中加盐拌上劲，加干淀粉、鸡蛋清拌匀，待用。

②豆瓣酱和花椒捣碎，待用。白糖、姜末、味精、酱油、湿淀粉、清汤放在碗中，调成芡汁。

③炒锅烧热，加油烧至五成热时，投入肉片滑炒至熟，倒入漏勺中沥油。

④原锅加油 25 克，放入花椒、豆瓣酱，炒出香味，投入肉片，炒至红色，倒入芡汁，加辣椒油、芝麻粉翻炒均匀，出锅装盘。

特点：色泽红亮

口味：肉片鲜嫩，麻辣味浓郁

Spicy Sliced Pork

Ingredients:

250 grams (0.55 lb) pork tenderloin
1 egg white
1 gram (1/4 tsp) Chinese prickly ash
5 grams (1/6 oz) chopped ginger
10 grams (2 tsp) ground sesame powder from pre-baked sesame
1 gram (1/4 tsp) MSG
5 grams (1 tsp) spicy oil
10 grams (1 1/2 tsp) soy sauce
10 grams (2 tsp) soy bean paste
1 gram (1/6 tsp) salt
10 grams (2 tsp) sugar
5 grams (2/3 tbsp) dry cornstarch
5 grams (1 tsp) mixture of cornstarch and water
50 grams (3 tbsp) water
100 grams (7 tbsp) cooking oil

Directions:

1. Cut the meat into slices 5 cm (2 inches) long, 0.5 cm (0.2 inch) wide and 3 cm (1.2 inches) wide. Put in a bowl. Add the salt and stir until mixture becomes sticky. Add the dry cornstarch and egg white and mix well.

2. Grind the Chinese prickly ash and put aside. Put the sugar, chopped ginger, soy sauce, water and the mixture of cornstarch and water in a bowl to make a sauce.

3. Heat the oil to 110-135℃ (230-275°F) and stir-fry the pork slices until they are done. Take out and drain off the oil.

4. Keep 25 g (1 2/3 tbsp) of the oil in the wok. Put in the ground Chinese prickly ash and soy bean paste and stir-fry until they produce an aroma. Put in the pork slices and stir-fry until they change into a red color. Put in the mixed sauce. Add the spicy oil and sesame powder and mix well. Take out and serve.

Features: Beautifully shiny.
Taste: The pork slices are tender with a rich spicy flavor.

麻辣肉片
Spicy Sliced Pork

米粉蒸肉

主料:带皮猪五花肉 400 克

辅料:粳米 150 克

调料:葱段 25 克、甜面酱 40 克、姜丝 25 克、料酒 25 克、桂皮 2 克、酱油 60 克、味精 1 克、盐 1 克、白糖 20 克、丁香 2 克、大料 2 克

制作:①将粳米洗净沥干,与丁香、桂皮、茴香一同入锅,炒至黄金色后倒出冷却,磨成粗粉。

②五花肉刮洗干净,切成长 5 厘米、宽 3 厘米、厚 0.5 厘米的片放入盆中,加葱段、姜丝、酱油、白糖、甜面酱、味精、料酒拌匀,腌渍 1 小时,然后加入粳米粉拌和,使肉片均匀地粘上一层米粉。将肉片皮朝下整齐排在碗中,上笼用旺火蒸 2 小时取出。

③将肉翻扣入盘中即可食用。

特点:肉质酥烂,肥而不腻

口味:咸鲜

Steamed Pork Slices with Non-glutinous Rice

Ingredients:

400 grams (0.88 lb) streaky pork with skin
150 grams (0.33 lb) round-grained non-glutinous rice
25 grams (5/6 oz) sectioned scallions
25 grams (5/6 oz) chopped ginger
40 grams (2 tbsp) sweet soy bean paste
25 grams (1 3/4 tbsp) cooking wine
2 grams (1/15 oz) cinnamon bark
60 grams (3 tbsp) soy sauce
1 gram (1/4 tsp) MSG
20 grams (1 1/2 tbsp) sugar
2 grams (1/15 oz) cloves
2 grams (1/15 oz) star anise

Directions:

1. Wash the rice, drain off the water and bake in a wok together with the cloves, cinnamon bark and star anise until the rice is golden yellow in color. Take out, cool off and use a grinder to make into flour.

2. Cut the pork into slices 5 cm (2 inches) long, 0.5 cm (0.2 inch) thick and 3 cm (1.2 inches) wide. Put in a large bowl, add the sectioned scallions, chopped ginger, soy sauce, sugar, sweet soy bean paste, MSG and cooking wine to blend well. Leave to marinate pork for 1 hour. Place the meat slices neatly in a bowl with the skin side down. Steam over a high fire for 2 hours and take out.

3. Turn the bowl of meat upside down onto a plate and it is ready to serve.

Features: The meat is very soft, fat but not greasy.
Taste: Salty and delicious.

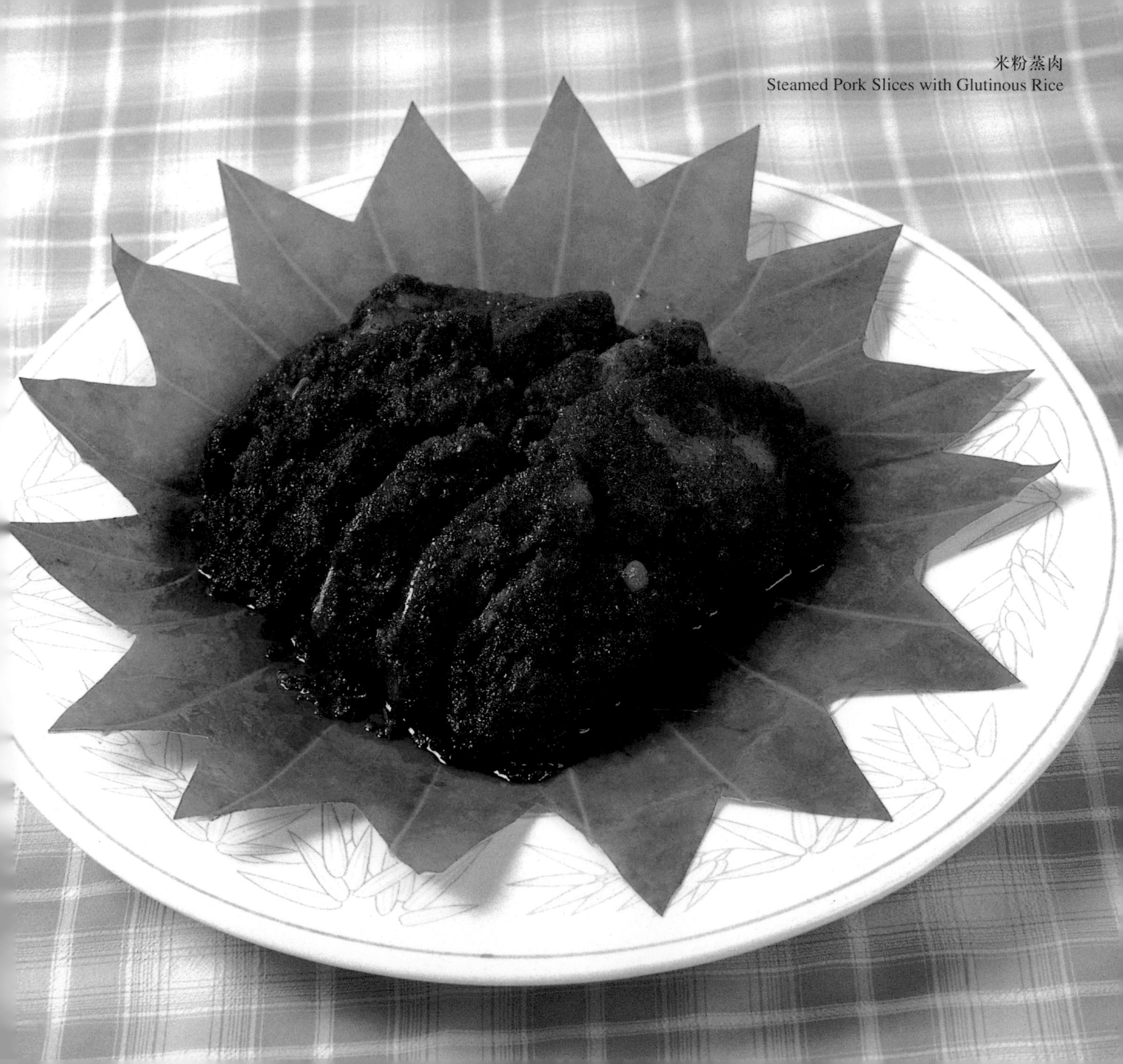

米粉蒸肉
Steamed Pork Slices with Glutinous Rice

辣子肉丁

主料:猪里脊肉 300 克

调料:干红辣椒 2 克、姜末 5 克、葱末 5 克、醋 5 克、蒜茸 5 克、料酒 10 克、酱油 5 克、白糖 10 克、味精 2 克、鸡蛋清 1 只、干淀粉 10 克、湿淀粉 5 克、油 100 克、盐 3 克

制作:①猪肉洗净切成 0.8 厘米见方的丁,加盐 2 克,干淀粉、鸡蛋清搅拌上浆备用。干红辣椒切成 3 厘米长的段。
②取一小碗,放入料酒、味精、湿淀粉、醋、酱油、白糖、盐调成芡汁。
③炒锅烧热加入油,烧至四成热时,投入肉丁滑炒至熟,倒入漏勺中沥油。原锅留余油 20 克,放入葱姜末、蒜茸、干红辣椒段炒出香味,倒入芡汁和肉丁,翻炒均匀出锅装盘。

特点:色味厚浓

口味:鲜辣可口

Stir-fried Diced Pork with Green Pepper

Ingredients:

300 grams (0.66 lb) pork tenderloin
2 grams (1/15 oz) red chili
5 grams (1/6 oz) chopped ginger
5 grams (1/6 oz) finely cut scallions
5 grams (1 tsp) vinegar
5 grams (1 tsp) mashed garlic
5 grams (1 tsp) soy sauce
10 grams (2 tsp) cooking wine
10 grams (2 tsp) sugar
2 grams (1/2 tsp) MSG
3 grams (1/2 tsp) salt
1 egg white
10 grams (1 1/2 tbsp) dry cornstarch
5 grams (1 tsp) mixture of cornstarch and water
100 grams (7 tbsp) cooking oil

Directions:

1. Cut the pork into cubes 0.8 cm (0.32 inch) long on each side. Add 2 g (1/3 tsp) of the salt, dry cornstarch and egg white and mix well. Cut the dry red chili into sections 3 cm (1.2 inches) long.
2. Put the cooking wine, MSG, mixture of cornstarch and water, vinegar, soy sauce, sugar and the remaining salt in a bowl to make a sauce.

3. Heat the oil in the wok to 70-100℃ (160-210˚F) and stir-fry the diced pork until it is done. Take out and drain off the oil. Leave 20 g (1 1/2 tbsp) oil in the wok and stir-fry the scallions, ginger, garlic and red chili until they produce a strong aroma. Put in the pre-prepared sauce and diced pork. Stir evenly and take out to serve.

Features: Richly flavored and beautifully colored.
Taste: Spicy and delicious.

辣子肉丁
Fried Diced Pork with Green Pepper

虎皮肉

主料：带皮猪方肉 500 克(注：方肉是指 15～20cm 见方的肋条肉)

调料：料酒 50 克、酱油 50 克、盐 2 克、白糖 25 克、葱末 5 克、大料 2 克、油 500 克

制作：①猪方肉洗净,用开水煮到八成熟取出趁热涂上酱油。

②炒锅烧热加入油,烧至八成热时,投入方肉炸至皮起泡有皱纹捞出,投入清水中浸软。

③将肉捞出,直刀切成 8 厘米长、1 厘米厚的片,皮朝下排放入碗内,加葱末、料酒、盐、白糖、大料、酱油,上笼蒸 1 小时至酥烂,取出。

④将汤汁倒入另一碗内,将肉翻扣入盘中,再将汤汁浇在肉上即可。

特点：皮色金黄,疏松多孔

口味：咸中带甜,香酥不腻

Tiger-skin Pork

Ingredients:

500 grams (1.1 lb) pork from the ribs, cut in squares 15-20 cm (6-8 inches) each side
50 grams (2 3/4 tbsp) cooking wine
50 grams (2 3/4 tbsp) soy sauce
2 grams (1/3 tsp) salt
25 grams (1 3/4 tbsp) sugar
5 grams (1/6 oz) finely cut scallions
2 grams (1/15 oz) star anise
500 grams (1 cup) cooking oil

Directions:

1. Boil the pork until it is 80 percent done. Rub with soy sauce when it is still hot.

2. Use a frying pan to heat the oil to 70-100℃ (160-210˚F) and deep-fry the meat squares until bubbles and wrinkles appear on the meat surface. Dip in clear water to soften the meat.

3. Take the meat out of the water and cut into slices 8 cm (3.2 inches) long and 1 cm (0.4 inch) thick. Place the slices in a bowl with the skin side down. Add the scallions, cooking wine, sugar, star anise and soy sauce, and steam for 1 hour.

4. Pour the juice from the bowl with the meat into another bowl. Turn the bowl upside down to place the meat and scallions onto a plate. Pour the juice from the other bowl onto the meat.

Features: The skin of the pork is golden yellow in color and the meat is soft with many small holes.

Taste: Salty with a slight sweet taste. Delicious, rich but not greasy.

虎皮肉
Tiger-skin Pork

五彩丝肉

主料：猪里脊肉 300 克

辅料：笋 50 克、心里美萝卜 75 克、青辣椒、红辣椒各 25 克、葱 15 克、姜 15 克

调料：鸡蛋清 1 只、盐 2 克、蚝油 10 克、酱油 5 克、胡椒粉 0.5 克、料酒 15 克、白糖 5 克、味精 2 克、干、湿淀粉各 10 克、清汤 100 克、油 100 克

制作：①猪里脊肉洗净，切成 6 厘米长、0.3 厘米粗的丝，加盐 1 克、鸡蛋清、干淀粉搅拌上浆备用。

②笋、萝卜、青红辣椒、葱、姜均切成丝。

③将蚝油、酱油、胡椒粉、盐、味精、白糖、湿淀粉、清汤一起放入小碗内调成芡汁待用。

④炒锅放火上烧热倒入油，烧至五成热时，放肉丝滑炒至熟，再放入笋丝、罗卜丝、青红辣椒丝、葱姜丝煸炒至熟，倒入碗内的芡汁，翻炒均匀，出锅装盘。

特点：色彩绚丽

口味：鲜香滑嫩，香味浓郁

Five-color Shredded Pork

Ingredients：

300 grams (0.66 lb) pork tenderloin
50 grams (0.11 lb) bamboo shoots
75 grams (2 1/2 oz) sweet pink-fleshed radish
25 grams (5/6 oz) green peppers
25 grams (5/6 oz) red peppers
15 grams (1/2 oz) scallions
15 grams (1/2 oz) ginger
1 egg white
2 grams (1/3 tsp) salt
10 grams (2 tsp) oyster sauce
5 grams (1 tsp) soy sauce
1/2 gram (1/10 tsp) pepper powder
15 grams (1 tbsp) cooking wine
5 grams (1 tsp) sugar
2 grams (1/2 tsp) MSG
10 grams (2 tsp) mixture of cornstarch and water
10 grams (1 1/2 tbsp) dry cornstarch
100 grams (6 tbsp) water
100 grams (7 tbsp) cooking oil

Directions：

1. Cut the tenderloin into thick shreds about 6 cm (2.4 inches) long and 0.3 cm (0.12 inch) thick. Add 1 g (1/6 tsp) of salt, the egg white and dry cornstarch and mix well.

2. Cut the bamboo shoots, radish, green and red peppers, scallions and ginger into shreds.

3. Put the water, oyster sauce, soy sauce, pepper powder, salt, MSG, sugar, and mixture of cornstarch and water in a bowl and mix for later use.

4. Heat the oil in a frying pan to 110-135℃ (230-275°F) and stir-fry the pork shreds until they are done. Add the bamboo shoots, radish, green and red peppers, scallions and ginger and stir-fry. Add the pre-prepared sauce and mix well. Take out and serve.

Features： Beautiful in color.
Taste： Delicious, slippery, tender and rich flavored.

五彩肉丝
Five-color Shredded Pork

红烧肉

主料:带皮猪五花肉 450 克

调料:盐 2 克、味精 1 克、酱油 75 克、糖 25 克、葱、姜末各 20 克、清汤 1000 克、油 50 克、料酒 20 克

制作:①猪五花肉洗净,切成 3 厘米见方的块。
②炒锅烧热放入油,烧至五成热时,放葱姜末炒出香味,倒入猪肉块翻炒几下,下料酒、酱油烧至肉上色,加清汤、盐、糖烧沸,转小火焖 1 小时,待肉酥烂再转大火收干汤汁,放入味精,出锅装盘。

特点:色泽红亮

口味:肉酥汁浓,咸中带甜

Braised Pork with Brown Sauce

Ingredients:

450 grams (1 lb) streaky pork with skin on
2 grams (1/3 tsp) salt
1 gram (1/4 tsp) MSG
75 grams (4 tbsp) soy sauce
25 grams (1 3/4 tbsp) sugar
20 grams (2/3 oz) finely cut scallions
20 grams (2/3 oz) chopped ginger
1000 grams (2 cups) water
50 grams (3 1/2 tbsp) oil
20 grams (1 2/3 tbsp) cooking wine

Directions:

1. Cut the meat into squares 3 cm (1.2 inches) long each side.

2. Heat the oil to 110-135℃ (230-275°F) and stir-fry the scallions and ginger until they produce a distinctive aroma. Add the pork squares and mix well. Put in the cooking wine and soy sauce, and cook until the meat changes into a brownish color. Add the water and salt to bring it to a boiling point. Turn to low fire and let it simmer for 1 hour. Turn to high fire to boil off some of the soup. Take out and serve.

Features: The dish looks invitingly shiny.
Taste: The meat is soft and the soup is rich. Salty with a slight sweet taste.

咕噜肉

主料：猪夹心肉 200 克

辅料：青椒 25 克、洋葱 25 克

调料：盐 2 克、料酒 15 克、番茄酱 50 克、糖 40 克、味精 1 克、白醋 3 克、清汤 25 克、大蒜瓣 2 粒、油 200 克、鸡蛋 1 只、咖喱粉 10 克、干淀粉 50 克

制作：①猪夹心肉洗净切成 2 厘米长、3 厘米宽、0.5 厘米厚的片，放盐、咖喱粉拌匀，磕入鸡蛋拌匀，腌渍 10 分钟后每块肉片均拍上干淀粉放入盘中。

②青椒、洋葱切 2 厘米见方的块，蒜瓣斩成茸。

③炒锅烧热加入油，烧至八成热时，分批将拍有干淀粉的肉片炸至外脆里嫩，倒入漏勺中沥油。

④原锅烧热倒入油 50 克烧热，放入青椒、洋葱、蒜茸煸炒出香味，再倒入番茄酱、盐、味精、糖、清汤烧沸，倒入白醋和肉片，迅速翻炒，使肉片均匀挂上番茄酱，出锅装盘。

特点：色泽红亮

口味：酸甜,香嫩

Sweet and Sour Pork

Ingredients：
200 grams (0.44 lb) pork
25 grams (5/6 oz) green pepper
25 grams (5/6 oz) onion
2 grams (1/3 tsp) salt
15 grams (1 tbsp) cooking wine
50 grams (2 3/4 tbsp) ketchup
40 grams (3 tbsp) sugar
1 gram (1/4 tsp) MSG
3 grams (3/5 tsp) vinegar
25 grams (1 2/3 tbsp) water
2 cloves of garlic
200 grams (2/5 cup) cooking oil
1 egg
10 grams (1 1/2 tbsp) curry
50 grams (3 1/2 tbsp) dry cornstarch

Directions：

1. Cut the meat into slices 2 cm (0.8 inch) long, 3 cm (1.2 inches) wide and 0.5 cm (0.2 inch) thick. Add the salt and curry, and mix well. Add the egg and let marinate for 10 minutes. Then dust every piece of meat with the dry cornstarch.

2. Cut the green pepper and onion into dices 2 cm (0.8 inch) long each side. Mash the garlic.

3. Heat the oil to 200-220℃ （390-430˚F） and deep-fry the pork slices until they become crispy on the outside. Take out and drain off the oil

4. Keep 50 g (3 1/2 tbsp) oil in the wok and heat it. Add the green pepper, onion, and mashed garlic, and stir-fry until they produce a strong aroma. Put in the ketchup, salt, MSG, sugar, water, vinegar and meat to quick-fry. Mix well to allow the meat to become coated with the ketchup. Take out and serve.

Features：Red and shiny.
Taste：Sour and sweet. Simply delicious.

咕噜肉
Sweet and Sour Pork

椒盐排骨

主料：猪大排骨 250 克

调料：料酒 10 克、鸡蛋 1 只、盐 4 克、味精 1 克、花椒 10 克、葱末 5 克、干淀粉 100 克、油 250 克、蒜茸 5 克

制作：①猪大排骨剁成 5 厘米长、2 厘米宽的条，用盐 2 克、味精、料酒腌渍 10 分钟，裹上鸡蛋液，拍上干淀粉待用。

②花椒上火炒熟磨成粉，加 2 克盐制成花椒盐，装入小碟内。

③炒锅烧热加入油，烧至八成热时，分批将拍上干淀粉的排骨炸至外脆里嫩，倒出沥油。

④原锅留油 25 克烧至四成热时，放入葱末，蒜茸炒出香味，倒入炸好的排骨，翻炒均匀，出锅装盘。随花椒盐蘸食。

特点：香味扑鼻

口味：松脆，鲜香

Fried Pork Ribs with Pepper Salt

Ingredients：
250 grams (0.66 lb) pork ribs
10 grams (2 tsp) cooking wine
1 egg
4 grams (2/3 tsp) salt
1 gram (1/4 tsp) MSG
10 grams (1/3 oz) Chinese prickly ash
5 grams (1/6 oz) finely cut scallions
100 grams (0.22 lb) dry cornstarch
250 grams (1/2 cup) cooking oil
5 grams (1 tsp) mashed garlic

Directions：

1. Cut the pork ribs into sections 5 cm (2 inches) long and 2 cm (0.8 inch) wide. Use 2 g (1/3 tsp) of salt, MSG, and cooking wine to marinate the ribs for 10 minutes. Mix them with the egg and dust on the dry cornstarch.

2. Bake the Chinese prickly ash and grind it into a powder. Add 2 g (1/3 tsp) of salt and put the mixture of pepper salt in a small plate.

3. Heat the oil to 200-220℃ (390-430°F) and deep-fry the ribs that have been covered with the dry cornstarch until they become crispy on the outside. Take out and drain off the oil.

4. Keep 25 g (1 2/3 tbsp) of oil in the wok and heat to 70-100℃ (160-210°F) to stir-fry the scallions and ginger until they produce a strong aroma. Add the pork ribs and stir well. Take out and place on a plate. Serve with a small plate of pepper salt.

Features：Has a strongly inviting aroma.
Taste：Soft, crispy and delicious.

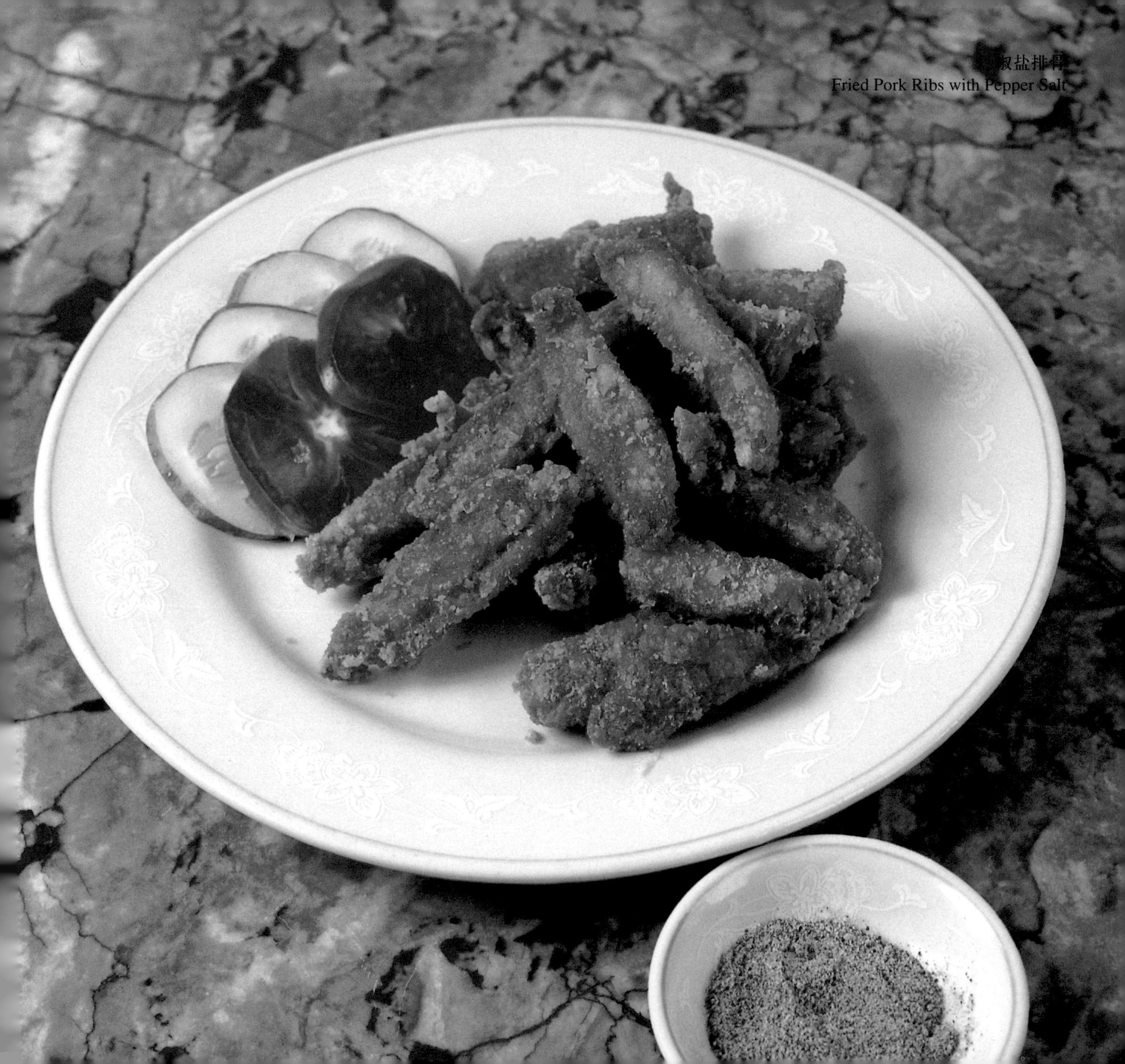

椒盐排骨
Fried Pork Ribs with Pepper Salt

脆炸肉饼

主料：猪肉末 400 克

辅料：面粉 150 克、水 75 克、发酵粉 5 克

调料：味精 1 克、盐 2 克、胡椒粉 5 克、油 200 克、辣酱油 50 克、葱、姜末各 5 克、料酒 10 克

制作：①肉末加盐 1 克、味精、葱姜末、料酒搅拌上劲，再加入胡椒粉拌匀，分成 4 份做成饼形，上笼蒸熟。

②将面粉、水、发酵粉、盐调成浆。

③将肉饼浸没在浆中，使其表面均匀地挂上浆。

④炒锅烧热加入油，烧至六成热时，转小火使油温保持在六成热，将肉饼逐个下油锅炸至金黄色，捞出沥油，再改刀切成小块装盘，随辣酱油蘸食。

特点：香脆酥嫩

口味：咸鲜

Deep-fried Crispy Pork Cakes

Ingredients：
400 grams (0.88 lb) ground pork
150 grams (0.33 lb) wheat flour
75 grams (5 tbsp) water
5 grams (1 tsp) baking powder
1 gram (1/4 tsp) MSG
2 grams (1/3 tsp) salt
5 grams (1 tsp) pepper powder
200 grams (2/5 cup) cooking oil
50 grams (2 3/4 tbsp) spicy soy sauce
5 grams (1/6 oz) finely cut scallion
5 grams (1/6 oz) chopped ginger
10 grams (2 tsp) cooking wine

Directions：
1. Add 1 g (1/6 tsp) of the salt, MSG, scallion, ginger and cooking wine to the ground meat and stir well until mixture becomes elastic. Add the pepper powder and mix well. Divide into four cakes and steam until they are done.

2. Use water, flour, baking powder and salt to make paste.

3. Soak the steamed meat cakes in the paste to allow them to be coated evenly with the paste.

4. Heat the oil to 137-170℃ (275-340˚F) and turn to a low fire to allow the oil to maintain this heat. One by one deep-fry the meat cakes until they are golden yellow. Take out and drain off the oil. Cut the cakes into small pieces and place on a plate. Serve with the spicy soy sauce.

Features： Crispy and tender.
Taste： Salty and delicious.

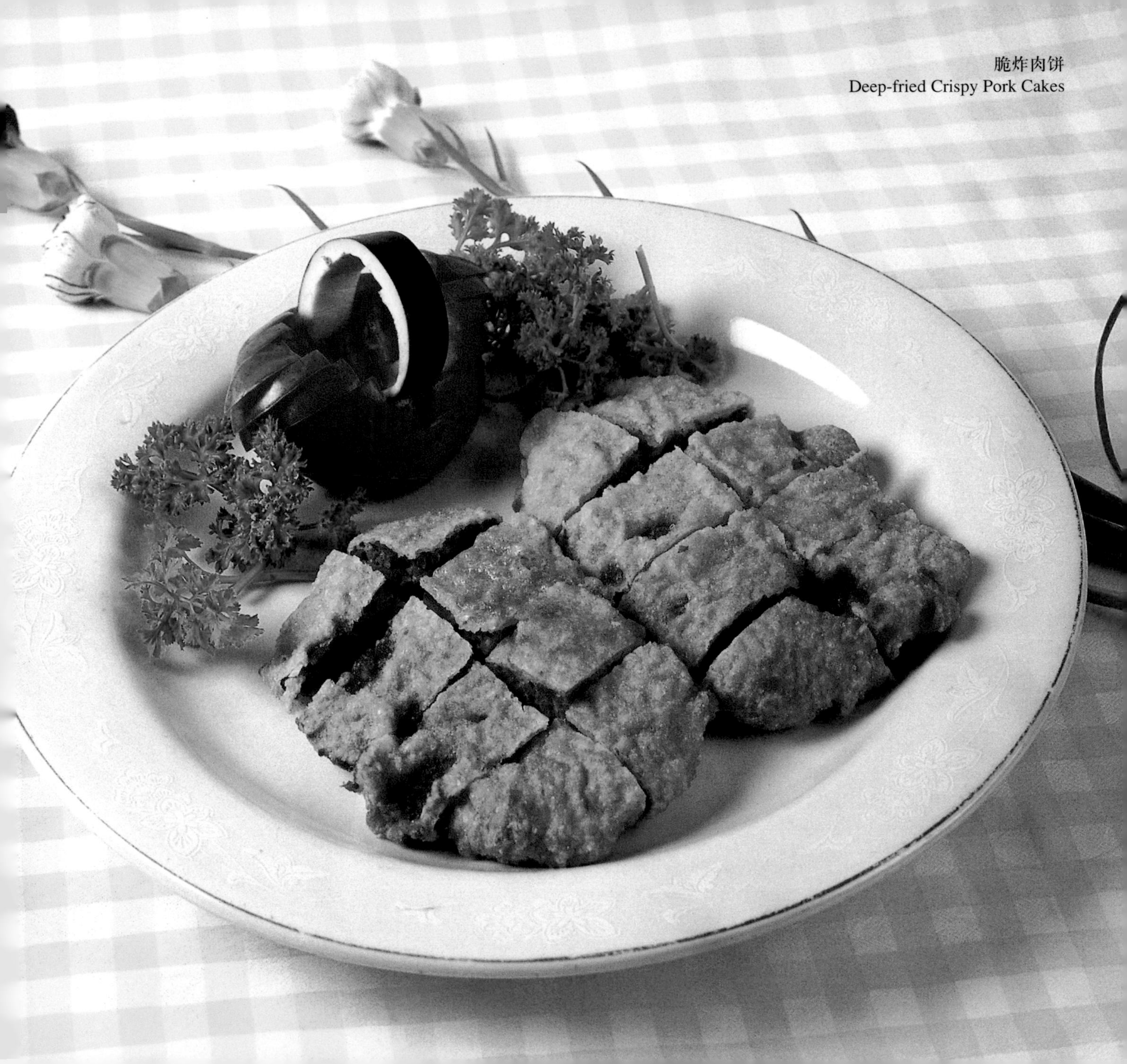

脆炸肉饼
Deep-fried Crispy Pork Cakes

鱼香肉丝

主料：猪里脊肉 350 克

调料：葱丝 50 克、姜丝 25 克、泡红辣椒丝 10 克、料酒 5 克、盐 2 克、酱油 5 克、香醋 15 克、味精 2 克、胡椒粉 2 克、蒜茸 5 克、鸡蛋清 1 只、豆瓣辣酱 5 克、湿淀粉 10 克、油 100 克、干淀粉 5 克

制作：①猪肉洗净切成长 6 厘米、宽和厚约 0.3 厘米的丝，加盐 1 克、鸡蛋清、干淀粉搅拌上浆备用。

②盐、酱油、香醋、味精、胡椒粉、湿淀粉一起放入碗中调成

芡汁。

③炒锅烧热加入油，烧至四成热，下肉丝滑炒至熟，倒出沥油，原锅留油 25 克，烧至四成热，放入葱丝、姜丝、泡红辣椒丝、蒜茸，炒出香味，倒入料酒、豆瓣辣酱，稍加翻炒，投入肉丝和芡汁，翻炒均匀，出锅装盘。

特点：色酱红而有光泽

口味：酸辣可口，香味扑鼻

Stir-fried Shredded Pork with Chili

Ingredients：

350 grams (0.77 lb) pork tenderloin
50 grams (0.11 lb) scallions cut into shreds
25 grams (5/6 oz) ginger cut into shreds
10 grams (1/3 oz) red chili presoaked and cut into shreds
5 grams (1 tsp) cooking wine
2 grams (1/3 tsp) salt
5 grams (1 tsp) soy sauce
15 grams (1 tbsp) vinegar
2 grams (1/2 tsp) MSG
2 grams (2/5 tsp) pepper powder
5 grams (1 tsp) mashed garlic
1 egg white
5 grams (1 tsp) spicy bean paste
10 grams (2 tsp) mixture of cornstarch and water
100 grams (7 tbsp) cooking oil
5 grams (1 tsp) dry cornstarch

Directions：

1. Cut the meat into strips 6 cm (2 inches) long and 0.3 cm (0.12 inch) thick. Add 1 g (1/6 tsp) of salt, 1 egg white and dry cornstarch, and mix well.

2. Use the remainder of the salt, soy sauce, vinegar, MSG, pepper powder and mixture of cornstarch and water to make a paste.

3. Heat the oil to 70-100℃ (160-210°F) and slippery-fry the meat strips until they are done. Take out and drain off the oil. Keep 25 g (1 3/4 tbsp) of oil in the wok and heat to 70-100℃. Add the scallions, ginger, red chili and mashed garlic, and stir-fry until mixture produces a strong aroma. Put in the cooking wine and spicy bean paste and stir several times. Add the pork strips and the pre-prepared paste. Mix well and take out to serve.

Features：Shiny with a brown color.
Taste：Sour and spicy to the right taste. Rich and delicious.

鱼香肉丝
Stir-fried Shredded Pork with Chili

糖醋肉排

主料：猪肋排 500 克

调料：酱油 50 克、料酒 20 克、白糖 50 克、盐 3 克、醋 30 克、湿淀粉 10 克、油 100 克、葱段、姜片各 10 克、干淀粉 100 克、清汤 50 克

制作：①猪肋排洗净，剁成长 5 厘米、宽 4 厘米的块，加葱段、姜片各 5 克、盐 1 克、料酒 10 克，腌渍 10 分钟。
②把腌好的肋排均匀地粘上干淀粉待用。

③炒锅烧热加入油，烧至七成热时，逐个投下粘上干淀粉的肋排炸至成熟，倒出沥油。
④原锅加油 50 克烧热，倒入料酒、酱油、糖、味精、盐、清汤烧沸，加醋，用湿淀粉勾芡，倒入炸好的肋排，翻炒均匀后出锅装盘。

特点：色酱红，汁光润

口味：香脆鲜嫩，酸甜可口

Fried Pork Fillet with Sweet and Sour Sauce

Ingredients：
500 grams (0.11 lb) of pork fillet
50 grams (2 3/4 tbsp) soy sauce
20 grams (1 3/4 tbsp) cooking wine
50 grams (3 tbsp) sugar
3 grams (1/2 tsp) salt
30 grams (2 tbsp) vinegar
10 grams (2 tsp) mixture of cornstarch and water
100 grams (7 tbsp) cooking oil
10 grams (1/3 oz) sectioned scallions
10 grams (1/3 oz) sliced ginger
100 grams (8 tbsp) dry cornstarch
50 grams (3 tbsp) water

Directions：
1. Cut the fillet into chunks 5 cm (2 inches) long and 4 cm (1.6 inches) wide and mix with 5 g (1/6 oz) of scallions and ginger each, 1 g (1/6 tsp) of salt and 10 g (2 tsp) of cooking wine, and marinate for 10 minutes.

2. Dust the marinated chunks of meat with dry cornstarch.

3. Heat the oil to 180-200℃ （355-390˚F) and deep-fry the chunks of meat, piece by piece, until they are done. Take out and drain off the oil.

4. Keep 50 g (3 1/2 tbsp) of the oil in the wok and add the cooking wine, soy sauce, sugar, MSG and salt and water, and bring to boiling point. Add the vinegar and thicken the soup with the mixture of cornstarch and water. Put in the deep-fried fillet and turn several times to allow the ingredients to be fully absorbed into the meat and gravy. Take out and serve.

Features：The color of the meat is brown and the gravy is shiny.
Taste：Crispy, tender, sour and sweet to the right taste.

糖醋肉排
Fried Pork Fillet with Sweet and Sour Sauce

木樨肉

主料：猪里脊肉 200 克

辅料：鸡蛋 3 个、水发木耳 50 克、葱丝 10 克

调料：料酒 10 克、糖 5 克、盐 3 克、味精 1 克、酱油 10 克、鸡蛋清 1 只、麻油 1 克、油 75 克、干淀粉 5 克、清汤 25 克

制作：①把猪里脊肉洗净切成 6 厘米长、3 厘米宽、0.3 厘米厚的片，加盐 1 克、鸡蛋清、干淀粉搅拌上浆备用。

②把鸡蛋磕入碗内加盐 2 克，用打蛋器打散。水发木耳用沸水氽一下，捞出控干水。

③炒锅烧热加入油 50 克，烧至六成热时，倒入鸡蛋液炒熟倒出。原锅加油 25 克烧热，投入肉片煸炒至熟，加料酒、酱油、木耳炒匀，加清汤煮沸，倒入熟鸡蛋、葱丝翻炒片刻，淋上麻油，出锅装盘即可。

特点：香嫩爽滑

口味：咸中带鲜

Stir-fried Pork Slices with Eggs and Fungi

Ingredients：

200 grams (0.44 lb) pork tenderloin
3 eggs
50 grams (0.11 lb) fungi, presoaked in water
10 grams (1/3 oz) sectioned scallions
10 grams (2 tsp) cooking wine
5 grams (1 tsp) sugar
3 grams (1/2 tsp) salt
1 gram (1/4 tsp) MSG
10 grams (1 1/2 tsp) soy sauce
1 egg white
1 gram (1/5 tsp) sesame oil
75 grams (5 1/4 tbsp) cooking oil
5 grams (1 tsp) dry cornstarch
25 grams (1 2/3 tbsp) water

Directions：

1. Cut the meat into slices 6 cm (2.4 inches) long. 3 cm (1.2 inches) wide and 0.3 cm (0.12 inch) thick. Add 1 g (1/6 tsp) of the salt, the egg white and dry cornstarch, and mix well.

2. Whip the eggs with 2 g (1/3 tsp) of the salt. Quick-boil the fungi and drain off the water.

3. Put 50 g (3 1/2 tbsp) of oil in a wok and heat to 135-170℃ (275-340°F) and scramble the eggs.

4. Put the 25 g (1 2/3 tbsp) of oil in the wok and stir-fry the meat slices until they are done. Add the cooking wine, soy sauce and fungi and mix well. Add the water to bring to a boiling point. Put in the scrambled eggs and scallions and turn several times. Sprinkle the sesame oil over the meat and serve.

Features: Delicious, succulent and tender.
Taste: Salty and tasty.

木犀肉
Stir-fried Pork Slices with Eggs and Fungi

宫保肉丁

主料:猪里脊肉 300 克

辅料:花生仁 200 克

调料:酱油 5 克、甜面酱 25 克、泡红辣椒 5 克、油 100 克、鸡蛋清 1 只、湿淀粉 10 克、干淀粉 10 克、料酒 10 克、盐 2 克、味精 2 克、葱、姜末各 5 克、豆瓣酱 25 克、糖 5 克、麻油 2 克

制作:①猪里脊肉洗净切成 1 厘米见方的丁,加盐 1 克,干淀粉、鸡蛋清搅拌上浆备用。

②将花生仁炸熟待用。

③炒锅烧热加入油,烧至五成热时,下肉丁滑炸至熟,倒出沥油。

④原锅倒入余油放葱姜末炒出香味,下料酒、豆瓣酱、甜面酱、泡红辣椒、酱油、盐、糖,倒入花生仁和肉丁翻炒均匀,用湿淀粉勾芡,淋上麻油,出锅装盘。

特点:色泽枣红,粒粒粘裹,酱汁紧包

口味:花生松脆,肉丁辣中带鲜

Stir-fried Diced Pork with Chili

Ingredients:

300 grams (0.66 lb) pork tenderloin
200 grams (0.44 lb) peanuts
5 grams (1 tsp) soy sauce
25 grams (1 1/2 tbsp) sweet bean paste
5 grams (1/6 oz) red chili, presoaked in water
100 grams (7 tbsp) cooking oil
1 egg white
10 grams (2 tsp) mixture of cornstarch and water
10 grams (1 1/2 tbsp) dry cornstarch
10 grams (2 tsp) cooking wine
2 grams (1/3 tsp) salt
2 grams (1/2 tsp) MSG
5 grams (1/6 oz) finely cut scallions
5 grams (1/6 oz) chopped ginger
25 grams (1 1/2 tbsp) soy bean paste
5 grams (1 tsp) sugar
2 grams (2/5 tsp) sesame oil

Directions:

1. Cut the meat into cubes 1 cm (0.4 inch) long each side. Add 1 g (1/6 tsp) of the salt and the egg white and mix well.

2. Deep-fry the peanuts.

3. Heat the oil to 110-135℃ (230-275˚F) and slippery-fry the cubed pork until it is done. Take out and drain off the oil.

4. Use the remaining oil to stir-fry the scallions and ginger until they produce a strong aroma. Add the cooking wine, bean paste, sweet bean paste, red chili, soy sauce, salt, sugar, peanuts and cubed pork, and stir well. Put in the mixture of cornstarch and water to thicken the soup. Sprinkle on the sesame oil and take out to serve.

Features: Red in color and every cube of pork and peanuts is wrapped in sauce.

Taste: The peanuts are crispy and soft, while the meat is spicy and delicious.

宫保肉丁
Stir-fried Diced Pork with Chili

腐乳肉

主料:带皮猪五花肉 400 克

调料:红腐乳 75 克、酱油 5 克、白糖 5 克、料酒 10 克、葱段、姜片各 5 克、味精 1 克、盐 2 克、油 50 克、清汤 500 克

制作:①猪肉洗净切成 4 厘米见方的小块用沸水氽一下捞出,洗净。

②红腐乳捣成泥状待用。

③炒锅烧热倒入油,烧至四成热时,投入葱姜煸出香味,放入肉块翻炒几下,倒入料酒、红腐乳和清汤煮沸,加酱油、白糖、盐转小火焖烧 1 小时至肉酥烂后加味精,转大火收干汤汁,出锅装盘。

特点:色泽鲜红

口味:肉质酥烂,咸中带甜,肥而不腻

Stewed Pork with Preserved Bean Curd

Ingredients:

400 grams streaky pork with skin on
75 grams (0.165 lb) red preserved bean curd
5 grams (1 tsp) soy sauce
5 grams (1 tsp) sugar
10 grams (2 tsp) cooking wine
5 grams (1/6 oz) sectioned scallions
5 grams (1/6 oz) sliced ginger
1 gram (1/4 tsp) MSG
2 grams (1/3 tsp) salt
50 grams (3 1/2 tbsp) cooking oil
500 grams (1 cup) water

Directions:

1. Cut the pork into cubes 4 cm (1.6 inches) long on each side. Then quick boil them and take them out to wash clean.

2. Crush the red preserved bean curd into paste.

3. Heat the oil in a wok to 70-100℃ (160-210°F) and stir-fry the scallions and ginger until they produce a distinctive aroma. Add the pork and turn in the wok several times. Put in the cooking wine, preserved bean curd and water and bring to boil. Add the soy sauce, sugar and salt and turn to low fire to stew for 1 hour. Add the MSG and use a strong fire to boil off some of the soup. Take out and serve.

Features: Bright red in color.
Taste: The meat is soft and salty with a slight sweet taste, rich but not greasy.

五香肉排

主料：猪大排骨 500 克

调料：五香粉 25 克、葱、姜末各 10 克、料酒 10 克、酱油 50 克、白糖 25 克、味精 2 克、油 100 克、盐 2 克、清汤 300 克

制作：①将排骨洗净剁成 4 厘米见方的块，用盐 2 克，料酒 5 克，腌渍 10 分钟。

②炒锅烧热加入油，烧至五成热时转小火，使油温保持五成热，放入排骨炸熟，倒出沥油。

③原锅留油 25 克烧热，投入葱姜末爆出香味，倒入五香粉、排骨、料酒、酱油、清汤烧沸，加白糖转小火烧 20 分钟，再转大火收干汤汁，出锅装盘即可。

特点：酱红油亮，香味诱人

口味：肉嫩鲜香

Spicy Pork Ribs

Ingredients：
500 grams (1.1 lb) pork ribs
25 grams (2 1/4 tbsp) five-spice powder
10 grams (1/3 oz) finely cut scallions
10 grams (1/3 oz) chopped ginger
10 grams (2 tsp) cooking wine
50 grams (2 2/3 tbsp) soy sauce
25 grams (1 3/4 tbsp) sugar
2 grams (1/2 tsp) MSG
2 grams (1/3 tsp) salt
100 grams (7 tbsp) cooking oil
300 grams (3/5 cup) water

Directions：
1. Cut the ribs into squares 4 cm (1.6 inches) long on each side. Use 2 g (1/3 tsp) of salt and 5 g (1 tsp) of cooking oil to marinate for 10 minutes.

2. Heat the oil in a wok to 110-135℃ (230-275˚F) and turn to low fire to maintain the oil at this temperature. Put in the ribs and deep-fry well. Take out and drain off the oil.

3. Keep 25 g (1 2/3 tbsp) of the oil in the wok, stir-fry the scallions and ginger until they produce a distinctive aroma. Add the pork ribs, five-spice powder, cooking wine, soy sauce and water and bring to boiling point. Put in the sugar and turn to low fire to cook for 20 minutes. Turn to a high fire to boil off some of the soup. Take out and serve.

Features: Dish is dark brown and shiny with a strong, enticing aroma.

Taste: The meat is tender and delicious.

五香肉排
Spicy Pork Ribs

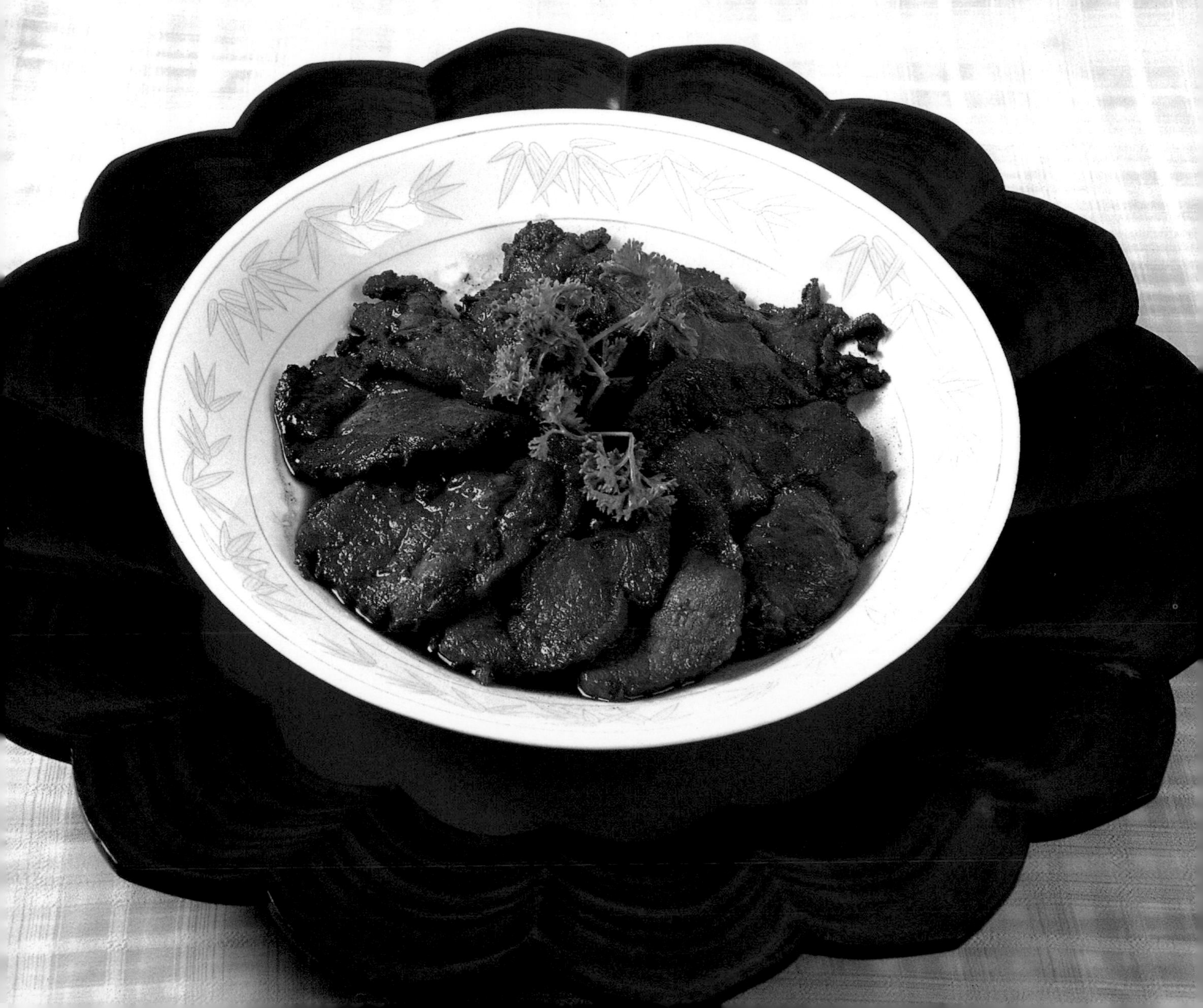

鸡蛋肉粒烩粟米

主料:罐装玉米 250 克

辅料:鸡蛋 2 只、猪里脊肉 50 克

调料:清汤 500 克、盐 5 克、味精 2 克、胡椒粉 1 克、油 25 克、料酒 5 克、湿淀粉 10 克

制作:①猪里脊肉洗净切成米粒状。将鸡蛋磕入大汤碗中打散。

②炒锅烧热加入油,烧至五成热时,下肉粒炒熟,加料酒、玉米和清汤烧沸,加盐、味精,用湿淀粉调好口味,趁热倒入有蛋液的汤碗中,边倒边用汤勺搅拌,最后撒上胡椒粉即可。

特点:色泽淡雅,营养丰富

口味:入口细滑

Diced Pork with Corn and Egg

Ingredients:

250 grams (0.55 lb) or a can of corn
2 eggs
50 grams (0.11 lb) pork tenderloin
500 grams (1 cup) water
5 grams (5/6 tsp) salt
2 grams (1/2 tsp) MSG
1 gram (1/5 tsp) pepper powder
25 grams (1 2/3 tbsp) cooking oil
5 grams (1 tsp) cooking wine
10 grams (2 tsp) mixture of cornstarch and water

Directions:

1. Cut the pork tenderloin into small cubes the size of corn grains. Whip the eggs in a large bowl.

2. Heat the oil in a wok to 110-135℃ (235-270°F) and stir-fry the meat until it is done. Add the cooking wine, corn and water and bring to boiling point. Put in the salt, MSG, and mixture of cornstarch and water. Turn several times and pour into the large bowl with the whipped eggs. Stir while pouring. Sprinkle on the pepper powder and it is ready to serve.

Features: Light and elegant in color. Highly nutritious.
Taste: Slippery and soothing.

鸡蛋肉粒烩粟米
Diced Pork with Corn and Egg

肉丝跑蛋

主料:猪里脊肉 150 克

辅料:鸡蛋 4 只

调料:料酒 10 克、盐 2 克、味精 1 克、葱末 5 克、干淀粉 5 克、油 150 克、鸡蛋清 1 只

制作:①鸡蛋磕入碗中打散,加盐 1.5 克和味精、葱末、料酒 5 克调匀。

②猪里脊肉切成长 6 厘米、宽和厚约 0.3 厘米的丝,加盐 0.5 克和干淀粉、鸡蛋清搅拌上浆备用。

③炒锅烧热加入油 50 克,烧至四成热时,下肉丝滑炒至熟,倒出沥油。

④原锅加油 100 克,烧至八成热时,倒入鸡蛋液并不断晃动炒锅使蛋液不粘住锅底,待鸡蛋液凝结成圆饼状时,均匀地撒上肉丝,将蛋饼翻转使肉丝压在锅底,晃动炒锅使蛋饼不致烧焦,然后再将蛋饼翻转,使肉丝朝上出锅装盘。

特点:色泽金黄

口味:鲜香

Shredded Pork with Egg

Ingredients:
150 grams (0.33 lb) pork tenderloin
4 eggs
10 grams (2 tsp) cooking wine
2 grams (1/3 tsp) salt
1 gram (1/4 tsp) MSG
5 grams (1/6 oz) finely cut scallions
5 grams (1 tbsp) dry cornstarch
150 grams (11 tbsp) cooking oil
1 egg white

Directions:
1. Whip the four eggs in a bowl. Add 1 1/2 g (1/4 tsp) of salt, MSG, scallions and 5 g (1 tsp) of the cooking wine and mix well.

2. Cut the meat into shreds 6 cm (2.4 inches) long and 0.3 cm (0.12 inch) thick and wide. Add 1/2 g (1/12 tsp) of the salt, dry cornstarch and egg white, and mix well.

3. Put 50 g (3 1/2 tbsp) of the cooking oil in wok and heat to 70-100℃ (160-210°F). Slippery-fry the pork shreds until they are done. Take out and drain off the oil.

4. Put in 100 g (7 tbsp) of the oil and bring to 200-220℃ (390-430°F). Put in the whipped egg and keep shaking the wok to prevent the egg from getting stuck to the wok. When a round cake shape of the egg appears in the wok, sprinkle on the shredded pork. Turn over the egg cake to cover the shredded pork. Keep shaking the wok so that the egg cake does not get overdone. Turn over the egg cake again to allow the pork shreds to come on top of the egg cake. Take out and serve.

Features: Golden color.
Taste: Delicious.

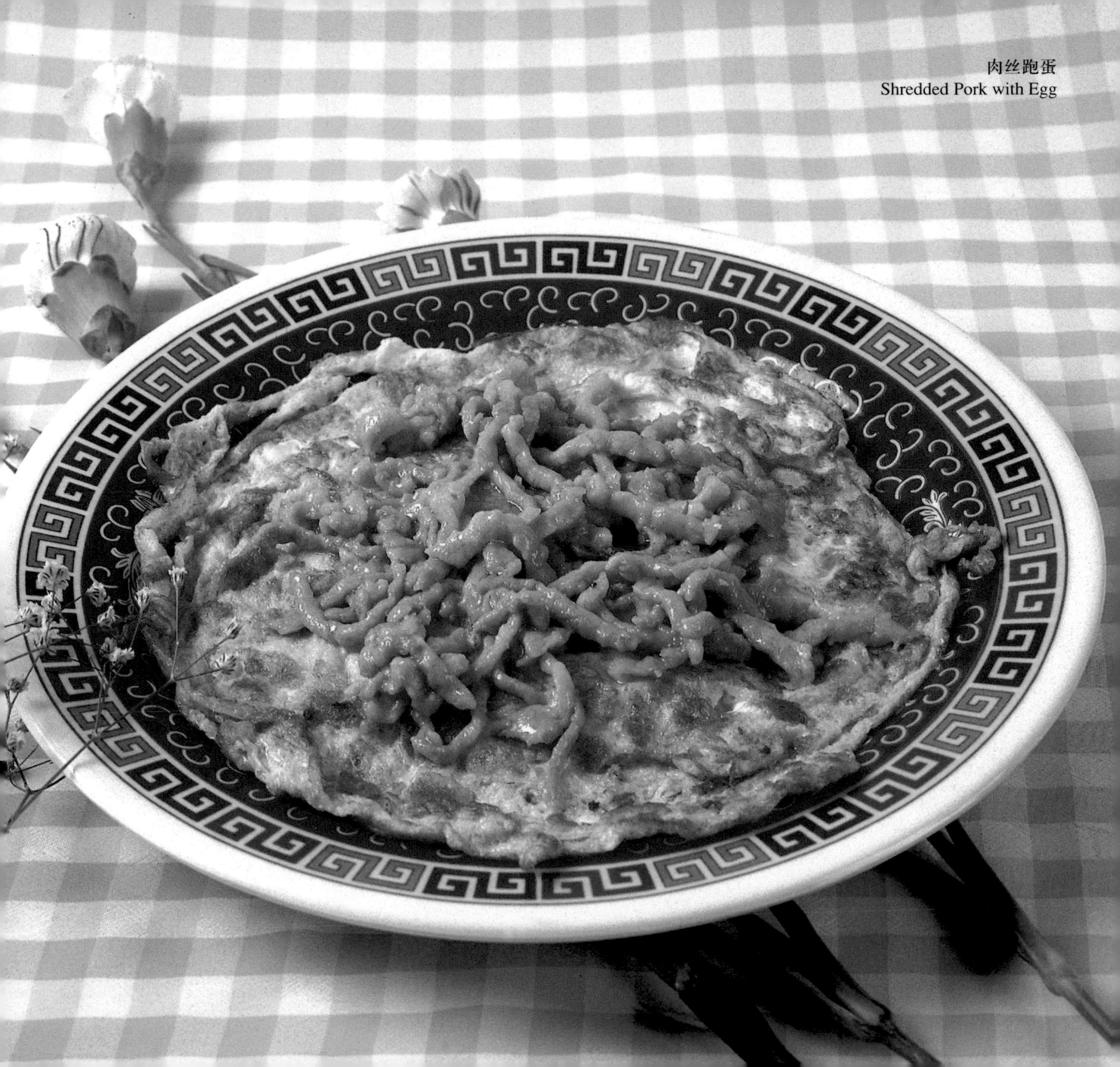

肉丝跑蛋
Shredded Pork with Egg

计量换算表

1 磅	1 盎司	1 打兰	1 格令
约 454 克	约 28 克	约 1.8 克	约 0.06 克

调料 / ml 勺	水	油	酱油	醋	料酒	盐	味精	砂糖	淀粉
1ml 勺	约 1 克	约 0.9 克	约 1.2 克	约 1 克	约 1 克	约 1.2 克	约 0.7 克	约 0.9 克	约 0.4 克
5ml 勺	约 5 克	约 4.5 克	约 6 克	约 5 克	约 5 克	约 6.3 克	约 3.7 克	约 4.5 克	约 2 克
15ml 勺	约 15 克	约 13.5 克	约 18 克	约 15 克	约 15 克	约 18.5 克	约 11 克	约 13 克	约 6 克
50ml 勺	约 50 克	约 55 克	约 60 克	约 50 克	约 50 克	约 63 克		约 42 克	约 20 克
500ml 勺	约 500 克	约 549 克	约 600 克	约 500 克	约 500 克	约 630 克			

A comparison of the weight systems

US system	1 grain(gr)	1ounce(oz)	1pound(lb)
Metric	0.065 gram(g)	28.35 grams(g)	454 grams(g)

A conversion table for measuring Chinese cooking ingredients*

ingredients cornstarch	water	ckg oil	soy sauce	vinegar	ckg wine	salt	MSG	sugar	cornstarch
1 pinch/1ml	1g	0.9g	1.2g	1g	1g	1.2g	0.7g	0.9g	0.4g
1tsp/5ml	5g	4.5g	6g	5g	5g	6.3g	3.7g	4.5g	2g
1tbsp/15ml	15g	13.5g	18g	15g	15g	18.5g	11g	13g	6g
1.76floz/50ml	50g	55g	60g	50g	50g	63g		42g	20g
3.52floz/1cup	500g	549g	600g	500g	500g	630g			

*All figures in grams given here are approximate as the exact equivalents will result in too many digits after the decimal point.

在编辑《学做中国菜》系列丛书的过程中，得到了苏州饭店的大力支持和帮助。作为苏州市旅游业的骨干企业苏州饭店已有数十年的历史，饭店拥有一流的烹饪厨师，经验丰富，技艺精湛。今借此书出版之机，我们对苏州饭店给予的支持，深表感谢!

We wish to thank the Suzhou Hotel, which kindly provided strong support and assistance to the compilation of the *Learn to Cook Chinese Dishes* series. As a major tourist hotel in the city of Suzhou, the Suzhou Hotel has a history of dozens of years and is serviced by experienced first-class chefs.

图书在版编目(CIP)数据

学做中国菜·肉菜类:汉、英文对照/《学做中国菜》编委会编. –北京:外文出版社,1999
ISBN 7-119-02491-4

Ⅰ.学… Ⅱ.学… Ⅲ.肉菜类-烹饪-中国-对照读物-汉、英 Ⅳ.TS972.1
中国版本图书馆 CIP 数据核字(1999)第 48187 号

First Edition 2000

Learn to Cook Chinese Dishes
—Meat Dishes

ISBN 7-119-02491-4

©Foreign Languages Press
Published by Foreign Languages Press
24 Baiwanzhuang Road, Beijing 100037, China
Home Page：http://www.flp.com.cn
E-mail Addresses：info @ flp.com.cn
　　　　　　　　sales @ flp.com.cn
Printed in the People's Republic of China

学做中国菜·肉菜类

《学做中国菜》编委会　编

© 外文出版社
外文出版社出版
(中国北京百万庄大街24号)邮政编码 100037
外文出版社网页：http://www.flp.com.cn
外文出版社电子邮件地址：info @ flp.com.cn
　　　　　　　　　　　sales @ flp.com.cn
北京骏马行图文中心制版
天时印刷(深圳)有限公司印制
2000 年(24 开)第一版
2000 年第一版第一次印刷
(英汉)
ISBN 7-119-02491-4/J·1515(外)
08000(精)